To Hell in High Heels

Helena Frith Powell is a regular contributor to the *Sunday Times*, where she writes the French Mistress column, as well as the *Daily Mail*, *Daily Telegraph* and *Mail on Sunday*. She now lives with her husband and their three children in the Languedoc region of southern France.

Praise for *Two Lipsticks and a Lover*

'Smart and funny'   Richard & Judy

'Witty, and very elegantly written . . . verbal
Viagra'   *Sunday Times*

'A fascinating – and illuminating – read'
                                     Daily Mail

'Funny, warm and charming'   *French Magazine*

Also available by Helena Frith Powell

Two Lipsticks and a Lover
Ciao Bella
More France Please

To Hell in High Heels

Helena Frith Powell

arrow books

Published by Arrow Books 2008

2 4 6 8 10 9 7 5 3

Copyright © Helena Frith Powell 2008

First published in Great Britain in 2008 by
Arrow Books
Random House, 20 Vauxhall Bridge Road,
London SW1V 2SA

www.rbooks.co.uk

Addresses for companies within The Random House Group Limited
can be found at: www.randomhouse.co.uk/offices.htm

The Random House Group Limited Reg. No. 954009

A CIP catalogue record for this book
is available from the British Library

ISBN 9780099517191

The Random House Group Limited supports The Forest Stewardship
Council (FSC), the leading international forest certification organisation.
All our titles that are printed on Greenpeace approved FSC certified paper
carry the FSC logo. Our paper procurement policy can be found at
www.rbooks.co.uk/environment

Typeset by Palimpsest Book Production Limited, Grangemouth, Stirlingshire
Printed and bound in Great Britain by CPI Bookmarque, Croydon CR0 4TD

For my mother:
Age cannot wither her.

'One should never trust a woman who tells her real age. If she tells that, she'll tell anything.'

Oscar Wilde

'What happens to a woman when she loses her looks? Nothing.'

Lord Carnarvon

CONTENTS

Prologue   1

Chapter One: The First Cut is the Deepest   11

Chapter Two: A Flexible Frenchman   31

Chapter Three: Putting on the Ritz   57

Chapter Four: A Cheaper Option   77

Chapter Five: Environmental Ageing   96

Chapter Six: The Ageless Town   116

Chapter Seven: To Jamaica with Love (Stress-Free)   144

Chapter Eight: No Woman, No Cry   160

Chapter Nine: My First Anti-Ageing Conference   175

Chapter Ten: An Encounter with a Laser   195

Chapter Eleven: The Botox Diary   210

Chapter Twelve: Ten Years Younger in Three Days   231

Chapter Thirteen: Still Getting Younger in New York   260

Chapter Fourteen: Luscious Lips or a Trout-Pout?   286

Chapter Fifteen: LA Women   307

Chapter Sixteen: Still Waiting for Lunch in LA   325

Chapter Seventeen: Laughing on Laguna Beach   342

Chapter Eighteen: Better Than Death   365

Chapter Nineteen: Conclusions   390

Acknowledgements   406

Prologue

'I see you're looking at my buttocks,' says my hairdresser, Fernando.

I wasn't; but I do now. They are round, full and pert. Now he's drawn my attention to them, I am tempted to lean over and stroke them.

'They're lovely, aren't they?' he says. 'They weren't always like this.'

Fernando explains that the last time he went home to Brazil he saw an old friend. This friend used to have a concave backside.

'Suddenly there he was in a bright red thong, prancing around the beach looking like the perfect specimen,' says Fernando. 'I asked what he'd done to himself. He told me nothing; that he'd been to the gym a lot. I knew that wasn't true. I used to live with him; he's lazier than I am. I went on and on at him and eventually he told me about a man who injects a substance to create the perfect shape. I made an appointment later that day and *voilà*!'

Fernando turns round and shoves his buttocks in the direction of my face.

'Magnificent, no?' he says. 'They used to be non-existent. Now I can finally wear tight jeans without shame.'

Fernando is busy cutting my hair. It's not a great job, being my hairdresser. I have long, thin, extremely fine hair that just hangs there. But he's trying his best to breathe some life into it.

He sees me looking in the mirror at an attractive lady seated behind us. She has thick, long blonde hair, perfect skin and long, shapely legs.

'How old are you?' he asks me.

'Thirty-nine,' I lie. I will tell Fernando anything, but not my real age.

'You see that woman?' he says, motioning to the attractive blonde. 'She's almost ten years older than you.'

I'm amazed. 'How do you know?'

'An ex-boyfriend of mine was her facialist at the Clinique La Prairie in Switzerland. She's forty-seven. I do her hair extensions. She looks good, eh? Almost younger than you.'

'I'm sorry?' I can hardly believe he said that. Did I hear him right or have I still got some shampoo in my ears?

'Don't be offended,' says Fernando, leaning closer to me. 'All I'm saying is you need to do a little work. You're an attractive woman, but your age is beginning to show.'

Although Fernando may not believe me, ageing is something of an obsession of mine. I may not have much time to think about it or indulge in it, but this desire to stay young for ever is in my genes. The last time I saw my father was on his eighty-fourth birthday. I had my son, Leonardo, with me. When Leonardo called him 'Grandfather' in front of a pretty young waitress my father nearly had a fit.

'Teach him to call me uncle or something,' he yelled.

'Why? You're his grandfather.'

'Being a grandfather presupposes you have to be older than someone else,' said my father.

'Well, *hello*? You are eighty-four today and he is two. There is an age difference that is pretty obvious to everyone.'

'That's what you think,' was his response. What could I say?

I remember when I was fourteen and went to stay with my aunt in her house on the Amalfi coast, and we bumped into a couple of women who were probably around her age. She was then in her mid-fifties.

'This is my little sister,' she said proudly, shoving me in front of them.

I was too amazed to speak. Looking back on it, I'm surprised she didn't tell them I was her older sister.

When I spoke to my father recently he told me that my aunt has finally got what she's always wanted: she has succeeded in becoming her own daughter.

'It's amazing,' he told me. 'She doesn't look a day over forty. Maybe it's all the fish she eats.'

This is a typical exaggeration by him, as always, but it does make you stop and think what a bit of surgery and sea bass can do.

I am not as obsessed about ageing as my mad relations, but I am more aware of it than most of my friends. One of my best friends, Rachel, and I were drinking Chardonnay recently at a wedding. Of course we're now too old to be going to friends' weddings; this was the wedding of the daughter of a friend of ours. We were standing around gossiping, feeling frivolous. Rachel's four children and my three children were all at home. We were out alone together for the first time in years. It was a lovely sunny day; we were merrily downing wine and wondering if we really shouldn't have a Silk Cut for old times' sake. It felt just like being back at university. In fact, this seems to be the main issue: my body and face just haven't kept up with my mind, which is still aged twenty. I feel the same age on the inside as I did when I first met Rachel over twenty years ago.

A good-looking young man walked past us. He had dark floppy hair and green eyes. He was tall and well built, probably twenty-five. Rachel caught me gawping at him and shook her head.

'It's no use,' she said. 'For us the war is over.'

What a horrible thought. Are we supposed to just sit back and passively let old age creep over us? Just lie there until we're covered in wrinkles and cellulite? I don't think so. Absolutely not.

'Personally, I'd rather go to hell in high heels than to heaven in flat shoes,' I told Rachel defiantly. 'You can wear slippers when you're seventy if you want to, but I shall be wearing Manolo Blahniks. Even if I'm in a wheel-chair.'

Later on, during the reception, I went to the loo. There was a girl standing next to me, young, pretty, glowing. Looking at our reflections in the mirror I was horrified. Next to her I looked positively ancient. I watched her leave the loo (briefly wondering whether I should push her down the stairs) and run into the arms of the good-looking young man I'd seen earlier. She didn't look old enough to be out on her own, let alone having sex, but then again to them I probably looked too old to be having sex. I got back to my table, determined not to let them depress me. Rachel and I drank and danced the night away, mainly to cover versions of songs we had danced to when they first came out. We might not have been the grooviest movers on the dance floor but, hey, at least we knew the words.

I look in the mirror. Even without my glasses on I can see that Fernando has a point. There are too many wrinkles on my forehead. And a particularly nasty one right in between my eyebrows. My skin looks sallow. If I smile there is a cluster of crow's-feet around my eyes.

For the last ten years I have been either pregnant or breastfeeding. My body has not been my own. And I haven't had the energy to do anything about it. Now my youngest child is three there is no excuse. And actually I no longer want an excuse. Sitting there gazing at my reflection, I realise that I actually care what I look like. In fact I can't believe I've let myself go to such an extent. *I* have to become a priority once more. There is a woman inside this mother wanting to get out again.

But I am also aware that three children have taken their toll and that if I don't act soon there won't be much point. But can I rely on Mother Nature to preserve me?

Historically she's not been kind to us girls. The crow's-feet around my eyes are only going to get worse. I'd never really considered it before, but if I can stop them spreading, why shouldn't I? Women all over the world have anti-ageing treatments all the time, every day. At any given moment, I've calculated, there could be up to a million women under the scalpel or needle. They can't all be wrong.

At the hairdresser's the woman behind me gets up to leave. She is thin and elegant. She looks great. But what would she look like without any help, I wonder. Maybe Fernando is right. Maybe I too could get some help. Hell, I might never have to rely on my own body again.

I could fly to Brazil and have a series of injections in my buttocks that would make them perfectly rounded. Cellulite could become a dim and distant memory as I parade up and down the Copacabana Beach in a thong. Then, if I wanted to, I could come back to London and have a boob job. There's nothing in particular wrong with my breasts, but once my buttocks were perfectly shaped they would probably need to catch up. In fact they could get bigger. I smile to myself: what a ridiculous idea. But then I start to think about it. Maybe not a buttock job, but what is so wrong with getting a little help in other areas?

Just think of all the treatments out there with the power to make you feel and look young. Perhaps by the time I hit my fiftieth birthday I'll actually look younger than I was when I was thirty.

'You must see lots of women who have had surgery,' I say to Fernando as the perfect blonde vision wafts out of the salon. 'Can you tell?'

'Sometimes it's so perfect I only know because I can feel the scars on their scalp,' says Fernando.

'So they look good on it?'

'Amazing. Really, I don't think any woman should age without a good surgeon by her side. It's just not necessary. Or polite.'

Easy for him to say – the disposable income in this place exceeds any normal person's annual salary by miles. But I wouldn't have to do it all at once. Maybe I could get a loan, a sort of anti-ageing mortgage. How much can a bit of Botox and a little collagen cost anyway? Now that everyone is being nipped and tucked, prices must have come down.

I know I'm getting carried away, but suddenly I am convinced this could be the beginning of the new me, a younger me. Ageing is inevitable but there must be something we can do to delay it. Why give in to age until it's absolutely compulsory? If I work really hard and try out everything that's out there, from age-delaying vitamins to Botox to facial peels and surgery, maybe I can avoid it, at least for another few years.

I share my plan for eternal youth with Fernando.

'Do it all,' he advises. 'But not the lips. I have never seen it work.'

Hmm. My lips are actually one of the first things I would like to change. Along with my thin, straight hair they're the feature I hate most about myself. But Fernando does have a point. I have an elderly relation who must be at least seventy but looks and dresses like a fifty-year-old. In fact she dresses like a twenty-year-old. Strangely enough she looks very good, apart from the trout-pout, which I think was an injection too far. I wonder briefly whether I should ask Fernando to cut me a fringe to hide the wrinkles on my forehead but decide against it. I am going to fight the wrinkles instead, banish them, become a younger version of myself. I will become the Gloria Gaynor of ageing; I will survive. My wrinkles, on the other hand, will not.

There are so many options available now. You can stay young through diet, alternative medicine, surgery, creams, collagen implants, microdermabrasion, microsclerotherapy and many other unpronounceable things. My aim is to try them all. Or at least research them all.

And then to pick the best of the bunch and laser/exfoli-ate/eat/implant/inject my way to eternal youth. I smile at Fernando in the mirror. It feels good to be tackling this problem (fore)head on, rather than just ignoring it and hoping it will just go away.

I ask Fernando for the name of that Swiss clinic the perfect blonde goes to again.

'Welcome to the world of the high-maintenance woman,' he says, writing it down for me.

I have a feeling this is just the beginning.

CHAPTER ONE

The First Cut Is the Deepest

I am dressed all in green. A lucky coincidence as my face is turning the same colour. I know this because the scrub nurse has just asked me in rather concerned tones if I'd like to sit down. I also have that awful pre-sickness feeling that I got to know so well as a child in the back of cars. The reason I am feeling queasy is laid out in front of me. She is a Ukrainian woman, I would guess in her late thirties, although it's hard to tell as the only evidence I have is a body covered in an iodine-based antiseptic and black pen marks where the incisions are to be made. She is lying on her front so I can't see her face. She is there to have work done on just about every part of her body.

I am here at the invitation of Dr Derder, head of plastic surgery at the Clinique La Prairie in Switzerland.

The clinic is my first stop in my much-anticipated quest for the best in anti-ageing and when Dr Derder mentions that he is about to perform a breast implant removal, a breast-lift, liposuction and a nose job all on the same woman, and asks whether I'd like to watch, I tell him I'd love to. As a child I was desperate to become a surgeon, but was no good at maths or sciences. I imagined myself wafting into operating theatres efficiently saving lives and calling for scalpels. I normally have to satiate my surgical fantasies with *Grey's Anatomy*; now here is a real-live operation, with a real-live Dr McDreamy. I am also keen to see cosmetic surgery in action as it is one of the options I am considering doing myself during my anti-ageing quest. I say 'considering' because at the moment it's way down on my list of possible options, and getting lower by the minute.

'Scalpel,' says Dr Derder. He makes four small incisions.

'That's where the cannula will go,' Penny, the English scrub nurse, tells me.

'The what?'

'It's a metal tube with holes in the end which dislodges the subcutaneous fat and sends it down the tube into the canister there.'

Penny points at a see-through container not unlike a

measuring jug. Already a blood-and-fat-speckled mixture has started to arrive. The fat is a deep cream colour, not dissimilar to something you might use for cooking. Dr Derder is pounding away at the woman's hips, bringing the cannula up and down with speed and strength; at one stage I think the cannula is going to go right through her skin. It looks like hard work. Maybe if the Ukrainian had made a habit of moving with the vigour that Dr Derder does now she wouldn't be in this mess.

'What happens to the fat?' I ask Penny, who has worked at the clinic for fourteen years.

'We throw it away most of the time, but sometimes it's used to inject into the patient's face.'

Sounds charming. But apparently 'fat grafting', as it's called, is very popular. I have already discovered, although I am only at the beginning of my journey into anti-ageing, that as we age, our faces lose volume and basically everything starts to sink until it all ends up around our jaw-line. Those concave areas we can fill with our own fat. I suppose it's better than someone else's. But it reminds me slightly of the idea of eating one's placenta.

Dr Derder has fine features and brown eyes. He is dressed in green surgical kit, which in my opinion makes anyone irresistible, but even without the strange green clothes he would be attractive, with smooth skin and the most delicate hands I have ever seen on a man. He looks as if he could have been a concert pianist.

He has been at the clinic for eight years. His father is Algerian and his mother Swiss, but he was educated in England so speaks perfect English. He tells me he is forty but he looks about twenty-five. This is something I have noticed with the staff at the clinic after just a few hours there: they all look at least fifteen years younger than they are. And they all have alarmingly white teeth.

'Have you had anything done?' I asked him before the surgery.

'Not yet,' he laughed. 'I was thinking of hair implants but decided to shave it all off instead.'

It was a good decision. He looks extremely elegant with his shaved head, and it must be more hygienic. I notice he still wears a skullcap, though. I don't have a skullcap; I have a kind of green paper shower cap, which is even less glam than a normal shower cap.

Dr Derder now shows me the difference between the part just above the patient's hip that he's done and the other one.

'Look at it now, before the swelling begins. You see the difference?'

I do. But the poor woman was quite thin to begin with, I protest.

14

'Liposuction is not for fat people,' says Dr Derder. 'It is for people with fat deposits they can't shift.' Aha. Now you're talking.

'It's extremely painful,' says Penny. 'There is a lot of internal bruising; she will have to wear a corset for two weeks.'

I look at the body laid out cold. Wouldn't you have to be pretty desperate to put yourself through this, just to get rid of some fat? She has a subtle tattoo at the base of her back; a shape I don't recognise. I ask Dr Derder if he's going to remove that along with her fat deposits and implants.

'No, she likes her tattoo,' he says.

The liposuction goes on for a while. It seems to be largely a lot of poking about. By the time he's finished, Dr Derder has extracted almost a litre of fat into the plastic canister.

The pop group Queen is playing in the background. Appropriately as they used to record their songs in nearby Montreux. There is even a gawdy statue in memory of Freddie Mercury on the shore of the lake.

'Dr Derder likes his music,' says Penny, 'but he doesn't get to decide what gets played. We do that.'

I leave them to begin work on the woman's breasts and decide to explore the rest of the clinic.

'Come back for the breast-lift,' says Dr Derder.

'It's a date,' I tell him.

The Clinique La Prairie on the shores of Lake Geneva is one of the most famous places in the world for anti-ageing. It is the home of the CLP Cell Extract, a revitalisation treatment that is exclusive to the clinic and, according to the brochure, 'promotes vitality, enhances the immune system and combats the effects of ageing.'

It was in 1931 that Dr Paul Niehans, the clinic's founder and nephew of Frederick William III of Prussia, first used cellular therapy. He was called in to help a female patient in a hospital in Lausanne, who was hovering between life and death following the removal of the thyroid and parathyroid glands. Dr Niehans removed the parathyroid gland from a calf, cut it up into small pieces, and injected them into the woman. A few hours later she began to recover. She went on to live another thirty years, dying at the age of eighty-nine.

Encouraged by this, Dr Niehans began to use a cocktail of organs from unborn lambs to inject into patients who suffered from an organ deficiencies. Niehans' patients reported not just improvements in the organs he was targeting but also that they had more energy and felt revitalised, so he began to refine and develop what is now known as the CLP Cell Extract.

'It was not his intention at the beginning to create an anti-ageing product,' Yaël Bruigom, marketing and PR manager, tells me.

It was also not his intention to go public with his discovery until he had tested it on at least 5,000 patients. But in the spring of 1953 he was called to the bedside of Pope Pius XII, who had fallen ill. He successfully treated His Holiness with cell therapy and the news of the miracle cure from Switzerland travelled fast.

People began to flock to the clinic and its fame spread. Charlie Chaplin, Marlene Dietrich and King Ibn Saud of Saudi Arabia became regular clients. Dr Niehans retired in 1966 and died in 1971 at the age of ninety-one. In 1976, Armin Mattli, a Swiss banker and businessman, bought the clinic and created the famous (and expensive) La Prairie range of skin-care products.

The clinic has changed somewhat since Niehans' day. Now, instead of fifteen rooms with no bathrooms there are a total of fifty-nine rooms, some housed in the original building, called the Résidence, and others in the newly built Medical Centre and Château. All the buildings are linked by sparkling white underground passageways lined with glass cases advertising local shops. They are a testimony to the kind of clients the clinic attracts. There are shirts with garish patterns, shoes with large rhinestones and the *pièce de résistance*: diamond-encrusted dominoes. I am tempted to break the glass and steal them for my daughter Olivia, who is a dominoes champion, but the Clinic would probably lock me up and never let me out. Which, come to think of it, might not be a bad plan.

The Résidence, the original building where Niehans worked from, is as Swiss as you like. It could have been lifted straight from the lid of a box of chocolates: a nineteenth-century chalet with yellow blinds, neat balconies and that classic peaked roof.

The new buildings, however, are modern and impersonal. The reception area, where I meet Yaël, the marketing manager, is 4,500 square metres of polished floors, plush beauty cabins and floor-to-ceiling windows. All very smart and clean but to me it lacks the charm of the Résidence. It feels too clinical. We sit at the bar. Leather chairs are dotted about, and on the dark shiny wooden tables there are menus offering all sorts of healthy drinks. I opt for a fruit cocktail with carrot and ginger.

The clinic now provides a wealth of treatments, but the cellular injections are still the main reason people come here. Although the spa itself is enough reason to make the trip, in my view. I don't know how they do it, but every time I go to the swimming pool it is empty; it's as if they have everyone on a different timetable so they never have to bump into anyone else. The sauna is also always empty and, for once, as hot as I can stand it. (Being half-Swedish I often find saunas outside my home country a little wimpy; this one is steamy enough to impress a Viking.)

When Niehans started his cellular treatment he would inject patients with sixteen injections each visit. Now they receive just two. They normally come for a week and have medical check-ups the first two days. The injections happen on the third and fourth days. Rates, which include all food and board, start at 17,600 Swiss Francs per person (£7,500) for a corner room in the Château, and go up to £18,000 for the Imperial Suite.

It is the cellular treatment that costs the most. If you go to the clinic and opt for, say, a thalassomedical or relaxation package week, the price drops to £4,200 for a corner room and £7,600 for a suite, and includes many more spa treatments and other extras.

The injections are manufactured from the livers of the unborn lambs. 'They have chosen the liver because it is the first organ to reach its final state in the foetus and it also helps other organs to grow,' says Yaël. The sheep are kept at a farm in the nearby district of Fribourg. 'We have around two hundred black sheep,' Yaël tells me. 'And once the female gets pregnant she is taken to an abattoir behind the farm and killed. Then the foetus is brought to the clinic.'

I don't know how I imagined they extracted parts of the foetus without killing the mother but this news rather shocks me.

'How pregnant is she when she's killed?' I ask, taking a sip of my fruit cocktail to steady my nerves.

Yaël is very slim, elegant and blonde, dressed in a grey wool skirt and jumper. To me she looks extremely Swiss but she tells me her father is Dutch and her mother is French. Even if I didn't know she worked at the clinic I'd be able to tell from her teeth. She too has that whiter than white Swiss white chocolate smile.

She looks a little pained at my question. 'She is in the late stages of pregnancy. For me this is the difficult part of my job. I am a vegetarian and love animals. Thankfully the clinic has a lot of other things to offer too. And we are working on a synthetically manufactured alternative.'

'Like what? Genetically modified cucumbers?'

Yaël doesn't say.

The foetus is taken to the laboratory in La Résidence.

I ask if I can see it but am told that due to hygiene issues I can't. In the laboratory the liver is extracted and then put through a procedure that turns it into powder. It is then frozen. When it comes to injecting it into patients it is diluted into a water-like liquid. One liver can serve around twenty to thirty patients, who will normally be aged between forty and sixty, but rarely younger.

Frankly, this all sounds a bit too gory for me. I think I need to know more before I agree to try it.

Meanwhile Yaël has arranged several other anti-ageing treatments for me. One of them is a Thai massage. Used for more than 2,500 years, it stimulates circulation and metabolism, but the main benefit is said to be spiritual or at the very least holistic.

'It is good for internal balance, calm and regeneration,' says Yaël. More regenerating than the foetus injection, I want to ask, but don't have the chance before she skips off to her office, pointing me in the direction of the spa where my masseuse is waiting for me.

I've had lots of so-called Thai massages but an essential ingredient has always been missing: the authentic Thai masseuse. So I am delighted when a pretty, petite Asian girl with a long, black ponytail comes to collect me from the spa area reception. She is wearing a grey T-shirt and white trousers.

'Where are you from?' I ask.

'Thailand,' she tells me, showing me into one of the most atmospheric rooms I have ever seen. It is almost entirely lit by candles in the shape of orchids; there is a subtle smell of orchids, or maybe it's jasmine. Instead of one of those horrible massage beds there is a double-size futon-type bed on the floor covered in white fluffy towels and cushions.

Nittaya instructs me to undress and put on a tiny G-string made of paper. I don't know if it's the effect of being here or the smell of the orchids but suddenly I am really looking forward to this massage. I lie down on my front filled with anticipation, but I am not prepared for what Nittaya does next. It is so painful I let out an involuntary gasp. This woman has hands as strong as Frank Bruno and she's using them to pound my feet. When she moves up to my calf muscles I let out another groan of pain. I have spent three days walking around London in ridiculously high heels. My calf muscles are sore as hell. And she's not only pressing into them with all her strength, she's actually walking on them with what I think must be her thighs. To my dismay, she repeats the procedure five times, driving the pressure into the sorest bits.

I would like to say that it gets better, but my muscles

are so tight that it doesn't. I know she's only doing her job, and she's great at it, but by the time she gets to work on my neck I can only think of torture chambers. At this point, I'd rather age than endure any more. As a finale, she gets hold of one of my legs (I am on my back by now), bends it and crosses it over my other leg and then leans on it. There is an almighty crack and I almost faint from the shock. She reassures me that this is all good for me.

But there are some wonderful bits. The orchid oil she smears all over me smells divine and the gentle massage is a welcome relief after all the pummelling and prodding. Almost immediately, I can feel how much good she has done as my body begins to relax and enjoy the after-effects. There is one vaguely erotic moment when she straddles me and moves her knees in a circular motion on my buttocks which makes my whole body shift gently back and forth. At least I think it was her knees, from where I am it's hard to tell. She seems to have the most amazing agility.

This 'relaxing and regenerating' is all very well, but by now I am keen to get back to the operating theatre and into my cool surgical kit. I have grown rather fond of my outfit of vast trousers and top that could fit all my three children inside it as well as myself. It reminds me of a garment a rather eccentric English aristocrat called Lady Delamere once lent me to wear at dinner in Kenya. It was a bit like a tent. 'I call it my "indulge and bulge",' she announced, and instructed me to put it on. I have never looked less glamorous for a dinner party.

Getting into the green kit was possibly the most exciting bit. No, *the most* exciting bit was scrubbing in, which just sounds so professional. And I know from *Grey's Anatomy* that scrubbing in is the greatest honour if you're a medical student. It consists of washing your hands and forearms and then covering them with disinfectant. I text my husband, Rupert, to tell him about my new scrubbed-in status.

'Make sure they don't confuse you with the patient,' he responds. My husband likes his surgery on TV, not on his wife.

To complete my outfit I was given a pair of green plastic clogs (slightly last year, but we are in Switzerland).

In the operating theatre, Dr Derder has moved on to the breasts. I have missed the removal of the implants but there's plenty of work still to be done. The patient looks even more corpse-like than before, I think in part due to the iodine-based antiseptic. Her breasts have both been cut open to allow for the removal of the implants.

They have been tacked together (after some skin was removed to lift them) and the nipples float in flesh. It is not a nice sight and I am beginning to feel unwell again. I think it's the fact that underneath all the blood and open wounds her chest is actually moving in time with her regular breath. It just seems impossible that this woman is alive.

'The first time you see it, it's always a bit of a shock, dear,' Penny says reassuringly, staying close by in case I should fall over. I have never felt so comforted at the sound of an English voice.

What do I think of this woman who looks like a corpse laid out in front of me? To be honest, despite my own anti-ageing quest, I think she's rather sad. She has obviously started on a road she can't do a U-turn on and she is risking her life (OK, the risk may be minimal but it's still real) for the sake of vanity, which seems insane. But maybe if you have the money and the lifestyle, the way you look becomes so important that you will do anything to achieve what you perceive as perfection?

Of course, we all to a greater or lesser extent obsess about the way we look. I have only ever been truly happy with my breasts when I was either pregnant or breast-feeding and I would be lying if I said a breast enhancement isn't something I have thought about at some point. I have also considered the possibility of a breast-lift, should my rather undersized breasts start sagging with age. Small, saggy breasts is not a good look. So far I have been quite lucky, although after my first ever mammogram I noticed they were looking a lot less perky, as if they'd been flattened by the machine. After today's experience, though, I will just keep my fingers crossed that by the time they do sag someone will have invented a non-surgical breast-lift.

When I say the risk may be minimal, that, of course, isn't quite true. People have died from cosmetic surgery; the wife of the Nigerian president, for example, went to a Marbella clinic for liposuction and never came out.

Amazingly, this sort of tragic news doesn't seem to put people off. According to a survey published in the *Daily Mail* in February 2007, half of women in the UK want plastic surgery. Data by the British Association of Plastic Surgeons (rather brilliantly shortened to BAAPS) states that in the UK, 28,291 surgical procedures were carried out in 2006, a 31.2 per cent increase on the preceding year. Liposuction moved up the chart from eighth place to third place in the same year with an increase of 90 per cent on 2005.

Anti-ageing procedures in the UK (face-lifts, eyelid surgery and brow-lifts) continued to show a steady rise in popularity in 2006, increasing by 44, 48 and 50 per cent, respectively. In total, 92 per cent of procedures were carried out on women and only 8 per cent on men. These figures are paltry compared with America, where almost two million surgical procedures were carried out in 2006.

One of the scrub nurses asks if I'd like to feel the patient's removed implant. I don't really, but I figure I may never have another chance as long as I live, so I go for it. They are shaped a little like a half-moon, the rounded part being the bottom of the breast. Apparently the woman had never wanted a breast augmentation, she just wanted a lift, but her doctor in Ukraine told her he couldn't do a lift without one. According to Dr Derder that's not true and it is common practice to do one without the other. I wonder if her husband bribed her doctor back home. The surface of the implant is rough, rather like it's been sprayed with sugar. The colour is somewhere between cream and see-through. It is very squidgy, a bit like holding one of those stress balls but with a softer consistency.

Dr Derder is getting on with the time-consuming task of sewing the nipple back to the flesh.

'It's moved up by about four centimetres,' he tells me. 'If possible she doesn't want implants — she doesn't like the idea of them — so I have just taken away some skin and made them a lot firmer.'

I have to say, despite obvious disadvantages such as blood-soaked towels and black stitches, her breasts look in good shape right now. They must have been extremely ample with the implants in.

Dr Derder agrees with me. 'She's quite a small woman,' he says. 'She didn't need all that really.'

He begins by attaching the highest part of the areola to the surrounding skin. Then he does the same with the bottom part, then each side. After those first four stitches her nipple is looking like a flag, pinned to a mast in four directions. Then he begins to work his way around the bits in between. At one stage it looks like a small flower, with the blood of the flesh below acting as petals. It's all incredibly symmetrical. No wonder he is world-renowned. If I ever did decide on a boob job (very unlikely after today), he's my man.

I ask Dr Derder how many breast augmentations he does a week.

'About three or four,' he says. 'The thing with all plastic surgery is to meet the expectations of the patients as much as possible. If they trust you it's hard not to give them what they want.'

'How much will all this cost her?' I ask, nodding towards the patient.

'Around 30,000 Swiss Francs, that is about £13,000.'

'Is it really worth all the money and the pain?' I move forward to get a closer look at the stitching. Immediately Penny pulls me back. Apparently all the green paper around the operating table is sterilised and I'm not allowed even to brush by it.

'If it's going to make a real difference to her self-esteem and her quality of life, then yes I think it is worth it,' answers Dr Derder. 'I would never let someone just decide on plastic surgery as a spur-of-the-moment thing. I get patients coming in and saying I'll have this tomorrow, something else the next day and so on, but luckily, as we're booked up months in advance, I can't accommodate them. I'd rather they really thought about it and planned it. And it's never a good idea to have an operation because someone else tells you that you should.'

'Have you seen any horror stories?' I ask.

'Plenty. I have seen people with that sad-dog look that comes from surgeons trying to take too much skin from below the eye to get rid of the wrinkles. People with bits of hair in the wrong place due to a bad face-lift. The key to a successful face-lift is to keep the normal anatomical landmarks in place otherwise people will notice that something is wrong, even if they don't quite know what it is.'

'Do you think people are moving away from surgical procedures to non-invasive ones?' I ask.

'The thing is that they don't treat the same things, so they're complementary,' he says. 'If you want a wrinkle on your forehead treated, for example, that can be done with Botox.' I wonder briefly if he's looking at my most-hated wrinkle right in the middle of my forehead and pull my shower cap down a bit further.

'But if you're wanting to do something about your jowls, then that necessitates a face-lift.'

I can't imagine a situation when my jowls would inspire me to have surgery.

'Do you think plastic surgery can become addictive?'

'People seem to think they can keep going with face-lifts,' he says. 'The fact is there is no point in having more than two face-lifts. The skin just can't stretch that far. And of course there are people that come with ridiculous requests, but then I think it's just better that they go elsewhere.'

Two face-lifts? I'm not sure I could even cope with one. There have to be ways to remove wrinkles that don't involve scalpels or general anaesthetics, and I'm going to track them down.

CHAPTER TWO

A Flexible Frenchman

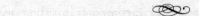

I am lying in a room overlooking Lake Geneva next to a handsome Frenchman who is telling me not to feel guilty. To make matters even more bizarre, he has his leg behind his ear.

'You must never feel guilty about relaxing,' Alain is telling me. 'Did you know that if you can breathe yourself into a totally relaxed state for ten minutes, it's the equivalent of ten hours' sleep? Imagine how good that is for the anti-ageing process.'

Alain is a yogi. He has dedicated his life to yoga and, actually, it shows. He looks amazing. His skin is clear, his eyes (one green and one grey) are bright, he has thick white hair and a grey beard. His body is perfect, his agility rather disconcerting.

'The thing about relaxing as opposed to sleeping,'

he continues, 'is that when you're sleeping your subconscious is still working. If you can empty your mind, which is what we aim to do when we relax, you can give your subconscious a chance to recharge. Many yogis I know only need about three hours' sleep a night. Now, let's sit up and I'll teach you to breathe.'

Since Niehans' day, the clinic has expanded and now offers all manner of anti-ageing treatments; but the core philosophy remains very much the same: treating ageing from the inside out. Hence the yoga.

One of the main anti-ageing benefits of yoga is that it helps you maintain flexibility of your joints and body. In fact there are some yogis who count a person's age not by the amount of years he or she has lived but by the flexibility of their spine. Yoga also firms up the skin, removes tension, strengthens muscles (and is especially effective for those awful flappy bits we all get on our arms as we age, known as bat's-wings). Some maintain that the inverted postures used in yoga can actually convert grey hair back to its natural colour. More realistically, yoga is hugely beneficial to your internal organs and can give you increased vitality as well as mental equilibrium and more resistance to illness. I am keen to try it as an alternative anti-ageing method to the surgery I have just seen. The results may not be as dramatic, but does it work?

When Alain breathes, he does so in three stages. He breathes in through his nose and first fills his stomach. Then he goes on to fill his ribcage and last of all, his chest. It's amazing to watch, rather like a snake eating a mouse. You see the shape of the breath filling his body. He makes a rather strange noise as well; the first time I heard it I thought he had taken a break from our yoga session to blow his nose.

'When you breathe out,' he tells me, 'always push just that little bit more. You need to be totally empty for the in-breath to be naturally flowing.'

We are sitting on mattresses on the floor of Alain's treatment room. The sun streams in through the window. In a mirror on the wall there is a reflection of faraway mountains and blue sky. Practically everything in the room is white, including Alain, who is dressed in white and has matching white hair. The only colour comes from the pink orchids in shallow vases that line the windowsill and the polished wooden floor. There is an incredibly Zen feel to the room. It is possibly the cleanest place I have ever been in.

At first I find the breathing totally impossible. I am gagging for air, I just can't breathe through my nose; this is totally ridiculous. I am a yoga failure. I pull myself together and try to focus a little harder. I firmly close my eyes. I concentrate on my breath. I draw it in slowly, down to my stomach. Alain shows me how to put my hand on my stomach so I can feel it move outwards. For someone who has spent most of her life holding her tummy in, this is an unnatural movement, but I go with it. The trick is on the out-breath. You need to push as much air out as you think is possible and then some more. If you can do that, the in-breath becomes easier. I know instantly once I've got it; my whole lungs feel used, I feel satiated but light-headed.

'You will probably feel a bit dizzy and maybe tired,' says Alain. 'That's normal.'

Alain says he is going to demonstrate a salutation to the sun, which we will then do together. I always find watching people do things like yoga slightly embarrassing, almost like watching someone on the lavatory. I cringe as Alain does some very serious breathing and goes into his salute to the sun. Then I have to stifle a giggle as he goes down into what's known in the trade as a downward dog and his little bottom sticks up in the air. But I have to hand it to him; he is fifty-six and moves like a twenty-year-old, leaping around on his mattress like a new-born calf, or even a new-born lamb, and you don't get many of those around here.

Looking at him, yoga clearly seems one way forward,

although I doubt many people have the time to make it such a big part of their daily lives as he does. I ask him if he thinks it has helped him to stay younger.

'It has changed my life,' he says. 'It is the best thing for you mentally and physically. It is extremely good for your internal organs. Not a day goes by when I don't cleanse my colon.'

We move on to the sun salutes. We do three on each side and then he tells me to do them alone; amazingly I remember the sequence. It is harder work than I imagine it would be. Maybe this is a good alternative to the gym. Exercise is essential to staying young and healthy, as we all know, and yoga seems an obvious choice; good for both your suppleness and strength.

One of the only other spas I have ever been to is Grayshott in Surrey, where Carla, a friend of mine, and I went for three days. She was there to write an article about it and I was there helping her research. Spas are not really her sort of thing. She prefers bars and thought it would be useful to have someone along who might know the difference between a sauna and a steam room. I remember going to a stretch class there. One of the people, a man of about fifty-five, could hardly move. There was nothing medically wrong with him but he was stiff as a board and his body was incapable of following the simplest instruction. Comparing him to Alain, who is around the same age, I can see how essential it is to move your body, and why people are drawn to yoga. But is it really enough to make a significant difference to how you age? It depends on how much you do. Anna, a friend of mine who is a yoga teacher, does at least an hour and a half a day, and it shows. She is forty-five but looks thirty-five. She is slim, fit and supple. Sadly I don't have time to do that much, but in the end whatever we pick I suppose the key is to do something every day, even if it's just a walk or a couple of sun salutes.

Alain tells me to lie down so we can begin the relaxation session. He tells me to breathe as he has shown me and works his way up my body – not literally, but he begins by telling me to relax my feet and so on until we get up to my face.

'If any thoughts come into your head, gently push them out,' he says. 'Think about nothing but your breathing.'

I feel more relaxed than I have in years. In fact, I don't remember ever feeling this relaxed, not even while I was asleep. We lie there side by side and just enjoy the peace of nothingness.

Dinner at the clinic is at 7.30 p.m. You choose your menu in advance from a selection of three starters, two main courses and three puddings. The maximum amount of calories they allow you to consume in any one day is 1,800. If you choose the low-calorie menu you'll consume even fewer. So there is no way you should consume more than this, unless, like me, you have a giant Toblerone hidden in your suitcase. Carla told me to pack alcohol, cigarettes and chocolate. I decided against the first two. 'I'm going to a health spa,' I told her indignantly. Mind you, this is a woman who showed up for our spa weekend with a hipflask of whisky and four Mars bars.

The dining room is in the same style as the reception area and it's vast. Dotted around the room are fifteen tables with cream and pistachio leather chairs around them. A line of lights that look like over-sized pleated skirts hang from the ceiling. The room is a bit too bright for me but the staff are warm and welcoming.

I am seated on a cream leather sofa at a table laid for one (Norma no-mates) with a white linen cloth and a large glass that is immediately filled with water. The waiter tells me the water is included and I ask for some wine. This water thing is something I have noticed before. It was the same at Grayshott Spa (which I do recommend as a more financially viable option than Switzerland, by the way): everywhere I went there was a little man offering me water. It was as if they had a secret mission to turn me into a water junkie. I found for days after my visit to both places I was constantly craving water. My body had got used to drinking more and I felt better for it. Sadly, as there isn't a little man running around after me at home constantly filling up my glass, this good habit has died, although whenever I think of the Clinique La Prairie or Grayshott I hastily gulp down some water, remembering that one of the keys to anti-ageing is to moisturise both inside and out.

The clientele in the dining room is varied, with the exception of the one thing they all have in common: they're all rich, paying a minimum of several thousands pounds for a week's stay.

To my right is a fat American man in a smart blazer, who is clearly never late for lunch as he is already ordering coffee and no one else has even started eating.

Next to him is a Russian couple, a mother and daughter, to whom I get chatting. I say 'get chatting' but a less chatty couple you couldn't hope to meet. The mother reluctantly moves her Hermès Birkin bag (at least now I've seen one) to make room for me when I ask them if I can have a quick talk. She is beautiful, but obviously of a certain age. It must be more difficult for very beautiful women to cope with age, hence perhaps the sullen attitudes. Fay Weldon once said about ugly women: 'And how, especially, do ugly women survive, those whom the world pities? The dogs, as they call us. I'll tell you; they live as I do, outfacing truth, hardening the skin against perpetual humiliation, until it's as tough and cold as a crocodile's. And we wait for old age to equalise all things. We make good old women.'

The Russians give hardly anything away, not even their Christian names, but I do manage to wangle out of them that this is their first visit, that they come from Moscow and that the mother is here for the cellular revitalising treatment. I am keen to hear more but they don't know much.

'We don't know if it works,' says the daughter. 'We heard about it from a friend of my mother's.'

'What is it supposed to do?' I ask.

'Give you more energy,' answers the daughter.

Her mother speaks little English. She is blonde and fine-featured. Her skin has that translucent quality that Cate Blanchett has, which I have always envied as a half-Italian olive-leathery-skinned person. She is wearing a cream and black Chanel tracksuit (I know because Chanel is written in big black letters all down the inside lining next to the zip; really classy).

The daughter tells me she lives in London and works

in private banking. They don't seem too bothered as to whether the sheep foetus thing will work or not and quickly start quizzing me about the best places to have Botox and nose jobs in the UK. In fact the mother only says two things to me and both are questions: where to get the best Botox and where did I get my cardigan, taking out her Hermès diary from her Hermès Birkin bag (why have anything else?) to jot down the details.

Now that the daughter mentions nose jobs I can see that her nose is rather dodgy. She is a less glamorous version of her mother, with mousy hair and broader features. I ask the daughter what happens in the evenings at the clinic.

'This,' she says looking around her. 'I'm already going mad, but she's having a nice time.' She nods at her mother, who sits there smiling. I wonder what the husband and father is like. For some reason I imagine a short, stout, rather bossy Russian oligarch with sweaty palms and not much hair, except on his back.

There are all sorts of people here – a lot of Russians, for some reason – for all sorts of treatments. A Chinese couple is here for their second visit, doing the injections.

'We believe in them,' says Frances, the wife, grinning widely.

Quite a few are seriously overweight, a couple from

Georgia, for example, who must be the fattest two people I have ever seen in real life. I'm amazed they managed to waddle into the dining room, let alone fit their tree-trunk legs under the table.

Weight loss is one of the major reasons people come to the Clinique La Prairie. One of the key factors to ageing well is eating well, and they are very strict on that here. They have a simple philosophy: every meal should contain something from each food group.

'Food must not only nourish and assure good health,' the nutritionist, Emmanuelle, tells me, 'it must prevent disease and ageing.'

Emmanuelle shows me a food pyramid and suggests I eat something from each section at every meal. It's a refreshing change from all those ridiculous diets where you eat no carbs or just live off some foul-smelling cabbage soup. So, for breakfast I have some bread or cereal, some fruit or fruit juice and some protein (egg, yogurt or cheese).

I ask Emmanuelle how eating well can help slow the ageing process.

'The key is to eat a balanced diet, not to forget to enjoy your food, to eat slowly and to chew well,' she says. 'And don't confuse hunger with appetite.'

*　*　*

On my third day at the clinic I have a meeting with Dr Roland Ney, a specialist in aesthetic medicine, which covers any medicinal treatments or procedures that change your appearance. As you might imagine, his office is perfect, his receptionist is perfect and the waiting-room floor is so clean you could eat your fondue off it. I am beginning to feel like I have walked into a Stepford-wife-style conspiracy. Everyone is so beautiful, so glossy, so happy that they just seem slightly unreal to me. Even the one patient I see in Dr Ney's waiting room looks immaculate. Maybe it's the sheep foetus injections.

The waiting room is all white except for the black floors. Even the coat-hangers on the polished chrome coat-rack are white. There is a glass display box promoting various beauty products from false nails to Restylane (a substance that fills wrinkles) to something called a Simonin machine. Perfect faces smile from brochures promising eternal youth and beauty, instant results and life-long perfection. There must be more to it than that, of course, but sitting there, you actually start to believe it. You start to think that you too could look like those smiling images.

But Dr Ney may be my first living proof that some of this stuff actually works. He has been at the clinic since 1995 and describes himself as a cross between a dermatologist and a plastic surgeon. He started off as a general practitioner and then moved into the aesthetic field, administering all treatments that involve lasers, injections, dermatological peels and checks. He is sixty but looks forty-five. I like him immediately. He is a warm, kind man with a sense of humour and a round, jolly face. His skin is clear and practically wrinkle free. His eyes and teeth are sparkling. Does the dentist here ever get a day off?

I ask Dr Ney how on earth he's managed to stay so young-looking.

'I climb 5,000 metres a year,' he tells me. 'Last year it was Damavand in Iran; in 2001 I climbed Ararat in Turkey. Also I have a personal trainer that comes to my office twice a week. I don't smoke, although I do drink; I like wine. My grandparents on both sides lived into their nineties so I guess a lot of it is genetic.'

'And have you had anything done?'

'Oh, yes, I take the CLP extract. I've been doing it for ten years. Last year I had a face-lift. I've had Botox as well and I take antioxidant food supplements. Not everyone agrees with me on that but the whole ageing process is oxidation so to me it makes sense to take antioxidant supplements.'

I guess at least they're not going to do you any harm.

Dr Ney has a few favourite procedures that he swears by. First and foremost Botox. 'It is the most powerful ageing prevention measure you can take,' he says. 'It is extremely safe and you should start around thirty. As with all aesthetic procedures, it's not the product that is dangerous, but the doctors.'

The other product Dr Ney uses is the Thermage machine. One session of one and a half hours lasts you up to two years but will cost around £2,000. If you're really keen to try it, it's worth flying to New York where it will cost you 'only' $2,500. The treatment is based on radio frequency. The doctor will treat your skin with a cube-shaped contraption, which emits gas to cool the skin followed by an electric current, which makes the fibroblasts (also known as rescue cells) beneath the skin's surface think the skin is being burned and rally to heal it. The idea is to get an increased cell activity and production of collagen, hyaluronic acid and elastin, the three elements that keep the skin looking young. One of the reasons it is so expensive is that the company that manufactures the cubed-shaped contraption charges £500 for each one.

'I've treated my mother with it and she's eighty-five,' Dr Ney tells me. 'But to be honest, it works better on people aged between forty and sixty before the skin is saggy and thin. Really by then the face-lift option is better.' I can imagine that if he's had anything to do with it his mother looks about fifty.

Dr Ney tells me that the Thermage treatment had terrible results to begin with. People came away badly burned and looking worse than when they went in. Now they have developed a method to cool the upper layer of the dermis while heating the subcutaneous layer at the same time, so you are unlikely to emerge looking like you've been in a car crash. In other words, it gives the body a signal that there is a burn without actually burning the patient. It doesn't really sound like something I want to try, mainly because it is so expensive, but also I'm not sure I like the idea of burning my face. They might call it a non-invasive treatment and I suppose compared with a knife it is, but how can you be sure it doesn't do permanent damage?

Non-invasive treatments have been around for ever. Cleopatra used to bathe in milk to make her skin soft and silky. That sounds fairly harmless. The nineteenth-century equivalent of Botox was paraffin, injected into the lines of the face. Sadly it was not as effective or as safe as Botox. The Duchess of Marlborough, for example, had it injected into her face when she was in her late fifties. She was a very attractive woman, a member of the Vanderbilt family, who had been encouraged by her social-climbing mother to marry the Duke in order to enhance the family name. Sadly for her, the paraffin hardened into long, hard grooves that drifted across her face and she decided to shut herself off from the world until she died. Why am I telling you this? As a warning to look out if you're trying something new – you may end up looking like a lunatic, albeit a young one. I ask Dr Ney the same thing I asked Dr Derder: are non-invasive treatments taking over from traditional plastic surgery?

'I think the way ahead will be mini-invasive surgery,' he says. 'For example, a small incision to raise the eyelid or lift the forehead. And, of course, fat grafting. Ageing is a change in volumes and now we can sculpt the face by injecting fat.'

'How much does that cost?'

'Between £1,500 and £3,000,' he says. 'But another technique I use is to rejuvenate the skin with a person's own cells. This method is called Isolagen. You take a piece of skin from behind the ear and send it to lab where they isolate the fibroblasts and clone them. Then you get millions of them back and reinject them. So while the Thermage machine stimulates them, this increases them by millions. If you have the two together, the result is wonderful. But of course if you have a face with a lot of sagging and very thin skin it will react less well, in which case you probably need a face-lift.'

'And what is the cost of cloning one's fibroblasts?' I ask. I have already heard of Isolagen. It is already gaining a reputation in the UK for being ineffective. In fact, there is a group of women suing the company for lack of results. They spent thousands of pounds on treatments and have seen no discernible difference.

'Around £6,000. But you know what?' Now he's really getting excited. 'You can keep the cells frozen so that you can use your own, younger cells say ten years on. You can cell-bank your own cells.'

'Hasn't this all gone a bit far? I mean, aren't we just becoming a little bit too obsessed?' I ask tentatively.

'Look, if you're a poor mother with three children, then you're not going to have the time or money –'

'I am,' I interrupt him. 'That's me.'

'But you're perfect,' he coos. 'You don't need anything.' Did I mention how much I like this man?

'Obviously it all costs money but if you don't have the money, there are things you can do, like eating well, not smoking, walking the children to school instead of taking the car, taking antioxidants. I think, really, exercise is the most important thing. There is no point in having the face of a thirty-year-old if you move like a sixty-year-old. It just becomes ridiculous.'

'At what age should we start doing all these treatments if we want to stay young-looking?'

Dr Ney smiles. 'We are ageing from birth,' he says. 'But the body is still going in a positive direction until twenty-five or thirty, and then things are stable for a while before they start decreasing so a natural time to start is in your late twenties. You have to think about prevention.'

'And do you think you will keep working until you're eighty, seeing as you look half your age?'

'Probably,' he says, leaping from his chair to say goodbye with the grace of a man half his age. 'Unless I die in a plane crash.'

I am walking to my next interview when my phone rings. It's Carla. I tell her about the injections and ask her advice.

'If you want my advice you should stop wasting your time. We all live far too long nowadays,' she says. 'Jane Austen died at forty-one – why is everyone so obsessed with living for ever?'

'If you'd died aged forty-one you'd never have met me,' I respond.

'You see?' she says. 'I told you all this longevity is overrated.'

I ignore her and ask if she thinks I should take the sheep foetus injections.

'Go for it. It can't be bad for you if all the Swiss are at it. They probably spread them on their Bircher muesli over there. As long as they don't make them out of dog foetuses I'm all for it,' she says. 'In fact, bring me some back for Tia. She's been looking a bit peaky lately.'

Tia is Carla's dog. I tell her I'll see what I can do and hang up. I don't agree with Carla's theory that we all live too long now. But I do think that we have to age well in order to enjoy life until the end.

Next I go and see the man who runs the clinic, Dr Thierry Wälli. Strangely enough for the head of the Clinique La Prairie, one of the first things he tells me is that 'anti-ageing does not exist'. Not exactly the hard-sell approach to his clinic's services.

'Surely if you come here and have a face-lift you leave looking younger?' I ask.

'This is the best place in the world to come and do anything from liposuction to a face-lift but please remember that cosmetic surgery does not make you one year younger,' he says. 'It changes you. And not always for the better. If I walk around in Miami I don't see much good advertising for cosmetic surgery.'

'What about your Dr Derder? He's very good.'

'He is a conservative man and he is also a very good salesman – not many people leave his office without agreeing to something. But, honestly, for me, it is not medicine, it is something totally different. It is something you buy, like a cosmetic you buy. Perchance Dr Derder is a doctor but in his work he tries to fulfil some wishes of his clients.'

In terms of pure anti-ageing Dr Wälli says there is only one thing you can do that will make a difference: a strong chemical peel that takes off the top layer of your skin and thus encourages new, younger skin to grow.

'But what about the famous injections?'

'They are not anti-ageing. They give you drive, they give you energy and better immune defence. Maybe you live longer, but basically you feel good which, I suppose, helps you feel and look younger.'

I ask him if he takes them.

'Yes, of course.'

'And do they help?'

'I think for someone in their late eighties I look quite good,' he says, laughing.

Joking aside, he does believe in the results from the cellular treatment.

'I know it makes me feel better and that it affects the immune system. For example, do you have genital herpes?'

'Not the last time I looked.'

'Well, it's a terrible thing,' he continues. 'Every month you have blistering on your vagina and it is very uncomfortable. But with our injections you can stop it. We all have the herpes virus but our immune system keeps it suppressed. When you get ill or tired, though, it can come to the surface, and there is no cure. Whereas one shot of CLP extract can change the situation completely. It has a direct effect on the immune system.'

He's rather a nice, old-fashioned man and even has normal-looking teeth. We talk about lots of other things, including his theory that in our society we are so bad at showing affection and touching each other that people go for pampering treatments to fulfil that human need.

I have decided against the injections. I just don't feel right about killing pregnant beasts just so I can have a spring in my step. Yaël the vegetarian is delighted and immediately sets me up with other anti-ageing treatments. I am going to try out a Simonin machine, like the one I saw in Dr Ney's waiting room. The principle is the same as the Thermage machine; it stimulates and regenerates the deep tissue, but unlike the Thermage machine you need several treatments. It is not as powerful and it is also a fraction of the price at £110.

My aesthetician is Parva, who, despite her Persian name, has always lived in Montreux. She is blonde and stocky, and I would guess around forty-five, but round here you never know – she could have celebrated her eightieth last week.

Before we start on the serious business of stimulating my fibroblasts I am led into a small oblong room with a sort of plastic growling creature in it that looks like a bath with a lid on it. The creature is making hissing and sighing and splurging noises. Parva has prepared a seaweed mixture, which she now spreads all over me. Then she lifts the lid and tells me to lie down inside it on a red rubber mat. She now closes the lid, which is a little disconcerting, and hangs a towel from the creature to my neck to keep the steam in. She tells me there will be lots of spurts of steam followed by sharp bursts of water, which will rinse the seaweed off.

'Don't be alarmed,' she says before she leaves the room. 'They're very sudden and very powerful.'

I lie back and try not to worry about the strange

noises. It wouldn't surprise me if the creature just suddenly opened up and swallowed me. But I am determined not to be taken by surprise by the shower. The room looks like it has been designed for an interior design magazine. Above me is a most intriguing hole in the ceiling, which I estimate is a metre thick. At the end of the hole there is a round window, which gives a view of the clear blue sky. I feel like a prisoner, gazing out of a small window in his cell. The seaweed mixture is warming up under the steam. I make sure I rub lots of it into my hands, which are always very dry. As far as jobs go, this isn't a bad one. I begin to nod off.

'Arrgghhhhhh, what the hell is that?!' I jerk awake, when suddenly I am being sprayed from all angles with freezing cold water. Parva is standing in the doorway, grinning. So this is how they get their kicks at the Clinique La Prairie.

Eventually I am released from the creature and taken through to a treatment room to be beautified.

The Simonin thing is painstaking work. Parva goes over my whole face and neck several times with a small gold contraption that looks like the wiry bit of a clothes peg. Then she changes the clothes peg for what looks like a miniature skate with two blades about the size of the small silver dog in the board game Monopoly. She uses this to carefully trace every one of my wrinkles. 'It stimulates the cells either side of the wrinkle and helps to fill it in,' she tells me.

Once all this has been done (about an hour later) she covers my face in an anti-ageing gel, and then uses another machine to blast this gel into my skin using pure oxygen that is pumped out through a mini-funnel.

After the treatments I feel cleaner than I have ever felt in my life and my skin is as soft as my baby son's. My face sparkles, it is radiant and fresh-looking, but my wrinkle is still there, glaring at me from the mirror, even if it looks a little less dehydrated.

The morning I am due to leave the Clinique La Prairie I am depressed. I wake up after ten hours' uninterrupted, blissful sleep in a clean bed someone else had made and enjoy my exquisite breakfast of Bircher muesli, freshly squeezed orange juice and Swiss rye bread. Later on today I will be home. My status will change from pampered VIP to mother/slave as soon as I leave the confines of the clinic.

To prepare myself for my entry into the real world I go for a walk by the lake. I haven't felt this good in years. In fact I don't think I've ever felt as good as this. Every inch of me feels clean, nourished, energetic. My skin is glowing and soft, my waist-line trim. I skip down the steps of the clinic towards the lake, wondering how I am going to keep up the good work they have started.

If you cross the road from the clinic and go left you will walk along one of the most beautiful stretches of the lake. In the morning a mist rises off it and you half expect Lord Byron to appear, wearing a silly hat and large shirt. Instead of Byron you get a wonderful mixture of birds: swans, ducks, geese and herons gliding around in the ice-cold water. Suddenly one of them will dive down and leave a trail of bubbles before he surfaces again. The morning sun reflects off the snow of the mountains, giving the light a magical quality. You could be in only one country in the world. About a five-minute walk from the clinic there is a square-shaped wooden jetty. You can walk to the end of it and admire the mountains, breathe in the clean air and enjoy the stillness of the water. It's the kind of view that makes you happy. I would defy anyone who suffers from depression to go and look at it. If it doesn't help, you may as well give up; I can't think what else could be done for you.

On my way back, I think about the various theories and ideas I have taken from the clinic. If you're going to take this anti-ageing looking-good thing seriously there is much to consider. Not only what you eat and how much you exercise, but how you cleanse, exfoliate, blow-dry your hair, as well as look after your feet and hands and elbows and knees, and just about every other part of your anatomy. Seems to me, by the time you've finished your head-to-toe regime it's time to go back to the bit you started on again. Toe-nails grow, as does hair on your legs. Eyebrows need plucking once every few weeks, for anti-cellulite cream to work you need to use it every day twice a day. Who on earth has the time to do all this as well as live? I suppose the trick is to do a little bit of grooming every day. And if looking after your skin is going to be a priority then you just have to make the time to do it. I am determined to do so once I get home. The washing, ironing, children's home-work, cooking and hoovering will just have to wait. Now I have started on this journey there is no going back. I suppose like most women I will learn to multi-task. Although ironing while painting my toenails could be tricky.

Reluctantly, I head back to the clinic limo, waiting to take me to the station and my train home. The real world, even in Switzerland, seems dirty and unpleasant. People's voices on the train annoy the hell out of me and I long for the serenity and cleanliness of the Clinique La Prairie.

CHAPTER THREE

Putting on the Ritz

For me the Ritz Hotel in Paris has always been linked with glamorous and ageless women. Here they have either aged gracefully, like Coco Chanel, who had an apartment there until she died; disgracefully, like the writer Colette, who danced on tables here as a septuagenarian; or not aged at all, as in the case of Diana, Princess of Wales, who ate her last supper here.

Every time I see that image of her coming out of the revolving door I want to tell her to go back and stay the night, rather like I always feel like telling Romeo that Juliet is really alive and there's no need to poison himself.

But it is a less radical method of anti-ageing than Princess Diana's that I am after as I walk through the Place Vendôme towards the hotel. I have decided I'm not quite ready to go home after my trip to Geneva. Instead I shall stop off at the Ritz spa to investigate the anti-ageing methods there. As I was passing through Paris anyway it seemed silly not to.

'It will save the expense of making another journey to Paris,' I reasoned on the phone to Rupert. 'I'll just be home a little later.'

'Don't worry, I'll just stay here and look after the children while you swan around spas,' he replied.

Well, if you insist . . .

I know very little about the Ritz spa except its clients include Liz Hurley, Sharon Stone and Jodie Foster. The only reason I know they are clients is that I happened to meet a masseur from Minneapolis on France's Atlantic coast a few months ago. He told me he used to work at the Ritz before he got married to a girl from the Île de Ré and moved out west. They were all on his client list and all incredible-looking. Since hearing this I have longed to go to investigate. The women I mention are three women of a certain age who still look great. I wonder if the secret to their success can be found some-where under the palatial façade of the Paris Ritz.

The Ritz building was constructed in the early part of the eighteenth century as a private house. It was converted to a hotel by the Swiss hotelier César Ritz and opened on 1 June 1898. The guest list reads like a *Who's Who* of the rich and famous. It includes Ernest Hemingway (who has a bar named after him where you can buy the world's most expensive cocktail, the Sidecar, which is made with an old Cognac and sells for €400. The man himself, at least in his youth, could only afford to drink here once a week), F. Scott Fitzgerald, Charlie Chaplin, Rudolf Valentino, Marcel Proust (who was nick-named Proust of the Ritz), Greta Garbo and King Edward VII. Contemporary guests include Madonna and Henry Kissinger. And of course Dan Brown's hero from *The Da Vinci Code*. Possibly the only reason not to go there. In 1979 the Ritz family sold the hotel to the Egyptian businessman Mohamed al-Fayed.

There are two doors in front of me as I stand before the hotel in the Place Vendôme. One is revolving and the other is normal. I walk through the normal one. It is not the most impressive hotel foyer I have ever been in, but apparently the original Mr Ritz decided against a large entrance hall to deter loiterers. It has an old-world charm, though, mainly due to its old-fashioned décor and slightly threadbare carpets, which you only find in places with a history. It is a grand hotel in the traditional sense of the word – marble, chandeliers, elab-orate flower displays, uniformed staff and high ceilings.

It reminds me of the Plaza in New York, which I once snuck into as a teenager on my first visit to the US. It seemed to me then the most amazing place I'd ever been to.

I walk down a flight of stairs to the Ritz Health Club, which was built by al-Fayed in 1988. I am unsure what to expect.

I am greeted by Alexandra at a rather small half-moon-shaped reception desk. 'Welcome to the Ritz Health Club,' she greets with a smile. She is one of those Parisians you just hate on sight: immaculate in a beige suit and cream shirt, not a hair out of place, and nails that look like they should be in an advertisement. 'Can I help you?'

'Yes, possibly by spilling something on your shirt,' I want to say, but instead I explain I have an appointment for a massage and an anti-ageing facial.

'Ah, yes, Madame Frith Powell,' she says beaming. 'Alexandra will be taking care of you.'

A medium-sized woman all dressed in white with dark hair tied back in a bun appears from nowhere. Her name badge confirms, she is also called Alexandra. Is this a prerequisite for working here?

The second Alexandra smiles and asks me to follow her. She is not wearing any make-up and her skin is clear. I take this as a good sign. She also has very white teeth – has she been to Switzerland recently? We walk through the reception area into a changing room with lockers lining the walls.

To say it is badly decorated would perhaps be unfair, but I don't think much of it. Alexandra gives me a heavy dressing gown. 'Take everything off, including jewellery, and put this on,' she tells me.

I obey her and then follow her into a darkened room. I have read somewhere that the Kiradjee massage I am about to have is one of Liz Hurley's favourites.

'It's a mixture of shiatsu, reflexology, massage, aromatherapy and pressure points,' Alexandra explains. 'It is a physical, mental and spiritual experience.'

Sounds good so far.

'We always offer an apple and lemon juice before the massage,' she continues. 'This is part of the cleansing process.'

I drink the chilled drink and lie down on a heated bed. The room is lit by candlelight and Alexandra starts to rub apricot oil onto my body. It smells wonderful; sweet and inviting. I fall asleep and wake up to Alexandra gently asking me to turn over. Then I fall asleep again.

'You have a lot of tension in your shoulders,' she tells me once the massage is over. 'And your intestines are not in a good way. You need to stop trying to control everything.'

Hang on a minute. This woman can tell I'm a control freak while I sleep? I look at my masseuse in a new light.

'Follow me to the facial care room,' she says. 'But get up very slowly.'

Meekly I do as I am told.

'Who will be doing my anti-ageing facial?' I ask.

'Me,' replies Alexandra smiling. 'You won't get rid of me that easily.'

Alexandra has worked at the health club for three years. I ask her what her top anti-ageing tips are.

'You need to use the right creams,' she says. 'And you need to use them regularly, day and night, all the time. That's the only way you will see results.'

'And which are the right creams?' I ask. 'I like Clarins personally.'

Alexandra shakes her head. 'Not rich enough. Here we use La Prairie.'

I might have guessed. A feeling of panic descends. This is going to be expensive. Added to my economic panic is that I read recently that Mick Jagger uses La Prairie caviar treatments. Do I really want to end up looking like him?

'What is it,' I ask Alexandra, 'that makes it so

special?' I am secretly hoping she'll say something stupid so that the spell will be broken and I can escape from this without spending more than my monthly mortgage payment.

'It works on the actual cells; it rejuvenates them, which no other creams do.'

'But surely if you've got a wrinkle, it's there for life?'

'Yes, up to a point, but a really good cream can reduce its appearance dramatically. It can change the surface of the skin, repair it.'

'But if you want to get rid of a wrinkle, surely the only way to do it is Botox or plastic surgery?'

Alexandra stops rubbing a heavenly smelling exfoliator into my face. 'I wouldn't recommend either,' she says very seriously. 'Botox is a poison, and especially for someone like you who has very sensitive skin I wouldn't like to predict what the consequences might be.'

'And what about plastic surgery? You must see a lot of women in here who have had it done?'

'Yes, a lot. And the odd thing is they all go to the same plastic surgeon, so they come out looking the same. It's most disconcerting. But again I would go for creams above surgery. A face-lift can give a person a very strained expression, one that really doesn't look natural. You can see the strain on their skin when they try to smile; it almost becomes a grimace.'

'OK, so no Botox and no surgery. So how am I supposed to stay young?'

'You cleanse every morning and evening, and for this the product doesn't matter – use Nivea, if you like. But the creams matter and you must use an eye cream as well as a face cream. You must also use a night cream. And don't forget your neck.'

The facial is lovely. There is something supremely enjoyable about having someone in a white coat fuss around you. Alexandra tells me I should have a facial at least once a month and then complement it at home with a weekly exfoliation and mask.

'Another thing to remember,' she says as she leaves the room, 'is that you can start the anti-ageing process young. Twenty-five for example is not too young; it will depend on your skin type.'

I lie on the bed covered in oil and creams, feeling slightly greasy, if very relaxed. The music is mellow and soothing, the light muted. It's really a rather nice place to spend a hot and sweaty afternoon as opposed to lugging myself around the streets of Paris. But how much difference has it made? I have spent around £200 on treatments today; will it be worth it?

Women have been having beauty treatments since Egyptian times, so I guess there must be something in it. Back then they involved rubbing oils and perfumes into the skin. The Egyptians believed in cleanliness and invented the concept of the spa. This was later adopted by the Greeks and Romans. The ancient Roman and Greek aristocracy spent a great deal of money on beauty treatments and beauty boxes to carry their make-up and jewellery around in, as did the ancient Chinese. We know that Viking and Saxon women carried beauty boxes too, because jewelled containers have been found in graves.

The concept of the beautician dates back to Ancient Egypt, where there were make-up artists for important people. Sadly some of the cosmetics were highly toxic, even causing slow death by poisoning, but at least the victims died looking good.

A couple of years ago a pot of Roman face cream was found in a Southwark drain. The tin contained a cream made out of refined animal fat, starch and tin. The marks where the Roman woman's (or man's) fingers had dug into the pot were still there. It was probably the cream that killed them; I can't imagine those ingredients would do you much good.

Using creams to prevent ageing is not new. An Egyptian papyrus from the sixteenth century BC contains recipes for dealing with signs of ageing like wrinkles and blemishes. The Greeks used what we now call face masks to improve the quality of their skin. They were made of flour and spices, and were washed off with asses' milk.

Nowadays it's much more complicated. There are millions of creams containing unpronounceable ingredients one has no idea what they are or what they do, like glyceryl polymethacrylate, phenoxyethanol and butylene glycol. Are these really substances you should be putting on your face? If you can't spell or pronounce them, are they safe?

According to Dr Nick Lowe of the British Skin Foundation, they are. 'All well-formulated cosmetics from reliable companies follow stringent guidelines about what ingredients they are allowed to put into creams and lotions,' he says in an article in the *Daily Mail*. But then he would say that, wouldn't he?

Creams all promise endless benefits. They claim to be nourishing, anti-ageing, tightening, anti-cellulite, lifting, firming, moisturising, soothing and a whole catalogue of other things. But the truth is that if they did what they said, none of us would ever age. There was a brilliant cartoon in *Private Eye*. A woman is at a beauty counter and there is a sign which reads: 'Anti-ageing cream 100% guaranteed.' 'It kills you,' the assistant is saying.

The most popular promise is that a cream is anti-ageing. This is what we all want. And if it says it on the pot it must be true, we think. Poor deluded saps that we are, desperate for help with our wrinkles.

So what really works? Just before I went to Switzerland, I spent a day with Tina Richards, a non-invasive anti-ageing consultant (this rather cumbersome title means that she is opposed to surgery and invasive anti-ageing methods and prefers more natural solutions) scanning the beauty counters at Harvey Nichols for the best creams.

'The fact is that no matter how lovely the packaging is, if an over-the-counter cream doesn't have certain active ingredients in it then it won't have any effect on your skin other than moisturising it,' Tina told me as we scanned countless products claiming to be rejuvenating, anti-ageing, revitalising, firming and proven to reduce wrinkles. 'Expensive creams with no active ingredients such as antioxidants or retinol only moisturise. Retinol and antioxidants actually do something that can change the appearance of your skin. Retinol, best used at night, stimulates collagen production. Antioxidants help to protect against free radicals.'

Examples of the antioxidants Tina was talking about are green tea, copper peptide, ferulic acid or idebenone.

Vitamin C is also an antioxidant and is good to help protect your skin. Tina advises, however, that not all these ingredients are suitable for every skin type; for instance some people with very dry sensitive skins cannot use a retinol or vitamin C without some irritation. They would be better suited to copper peptide to treat wrinkles, which in addition to being anti-inflammatory is an antioxidant and promotes collagen and elastin in the skin. So look on the list of ingredients for antioxidants when selecting a daytime product and retinol for night-time, but take your individual skin type into account; Tina recommends you get a sample size to test active ingredients first if your skin has a history of stinging, burning or reddening in response to skin-care products. My favourite out of the brands Tina recommends is the Philosophy line, although the serum which you mix with a vitamin C powder (Hope and a Prayer), can feel a bit strong. One of the Philosophy products I am mad about is 'Booster Caps', little green capsules filled with retinol that you mix with your night cream. It feels like you're covering your face with thick silk. The other products I adore are their microdelivery peel and the microdelivery exfoliating wash. Really smooth and comforting, they smell great too.

I have asked all the professionals I met during my

anti-ageing quest whether or not creams work, whether it's worth buying expensive brands or not. One answer I had was the most telling. 'Is this on the record or off?' said a dermatologist associated with a large cosmetic brand. 'If it's off then no, they don't really make a difference to anything apart from the surface of your skin.' Dr Wälli at the Clinique La Prairie agrees. 'What cream you use doesn't really make a difference, the main thing is that you moisturise.' Another dermatologist told me off the record that the only difference between, for example, Nivea and La Prairie is in the packaging. 'They are even made in the same laboratory,' she said. 'Just like Lancôme and L'Oréal.' A lot of dermatologists like the French brand Avène, which you can buy in pharmacies all over France for extremely reasonable prices.

The most expensive cream that I see on sale at Harvey Nichols is (not surprisingly) made by La Prairie. It is called Cellular Radiance Concentrate Pure Gold and costs £345. 'It looks delicious,' says Tina. 'I want to eat it.' The sales assistant hands us the pot of gold to try it. I am terrified I'm going to drop it. I smooth a tiny bit onto my hand. It feels incredibly smooth, really lovely, and leaves the skin glowing like, well, gold. Tina assesses the ingredients.

'It has some very good ingredients like algae and

ginseng,' she says, 'but none that will penetrate the upper dermis. I would say if money is no object then you could buy it for the feel-good factor but I personally wouldn't.'

One of the most-hyped products of recent years has been StriVectin, which started out as a stretch-mark cream and was then found to have a positive effect on wrinkles. This contains a palmitoyl pentapeptide (also known as palmitoyl oligopeptide) which is claimed to stimulate collagen and elastin synthesis in the dermo-epidermal interface layer of the skin as well as a retinol does and possibly as well as a prescription retinoid (known as a tretinoin).

'In my opinion palmitoyl pentapeptide in anti-ageing creams can plump up and have a smoothing effect on the very surface of the skin but does not do a better job than a prescription retinoid at reducing fine lines and wrinkles induced by sun damage, or over-the-counter retinol, for that matter,' says Tina. 'However, because palmitoyl pentapeptide does appear to have some positive effect on collagen and elastin synthesis and is non-irritating, it is one alternative ingredient for people sensitive to retinol and prescription retinoids.'

At one stage, according to the cosmetics buyer at Harvey Nichols, Tracy Van Heusden, StriVectin was the best-selling individual product in the store. Naturally when it first came out I fell for all the hype but it didn't make any difference at all. Tina says it is good for older dry skins as it contains sesame oil, sweet almond oil, cocoa butter and shea butter, which are very nourishing, but there have been no independent clinical trials that confirm it has a more miraculous effect on wrinkles than other brands.

A couple of interesting titbits I came away with from my trip through the world of creams and potions. Apparently putting collagen on the surface of your skin does absolutely no good at all. So don't fall for a cream with collagen in it. Also, as long as there is a sunscreen in a cream, the manufacturer has the right to call it anti-ageing. But in reality you may be able to get the same effect from a lesser-known brand sunscreen for a fraction of the price.

One cream that promises great things is based on your own DNA. It is called Dermagenetics and apparently used by all sorts of Hollywood stars. The process uses a swab from the inside of your cheek to create a personal anti-ageing formula based on your own DNA. The theory behind it is that most cosmetic creams are not suited to our genetic make-up and so the skin can't metabolise them. According to a spokesman at Dermagenetics, all over-the-counter products use the top ten anti-ageing ingredients to create skin creams and they don't necessarily agree with your skin type. With the swab you send to their lab, Dermagenetics test your genetic propensity for collagen breakdown, wrinkling and overall health. They then create a bespoke formula just for you. The base cream uses, among other things, lavender oil and citrus oil. The genetically selected ingredients include fennel extract, red algae extract and grape extract. Apparently Goldie Hawn, Meg Ryan and Teri Hatcher all use Dermagenetics, which may or may not be a recommendation, depending on how you think they look.

It was a pretty cheap-looking tube, to be frank, considering they're charging almost £125 for the product and £135 for the DNA testing. The product itself is nothing unusual; the smell is neither offensive nor pleasant. I didn't notice any huge change in the look of my skin but what I did notice was that every time I used it the top layer of my skin peeled off. I suppose this is good in terms of exfoliating, but I'm not sure it's healthy for it to happen every day.

The more I walked around Harvey Nichols the more I got the impression that most cosmetics companies are selling a dream, a vain hope that we can look beautiful for a few years longer just by spending £100.

When a woman buys a cream she must know deep down that putting gold on her skin, for example, is not going to keep her young. I have certainly bought creams knowing deep down that they really won't do what they say on the box. But in our desperation to fight our inevitable decline we hand over hundreds of pounds and ignore our rational selves as we indulge the side of us that hopes against hope that our wrinkles will magically disappear, or that at worst we will get no more wrinkles. In a sense it is all about survival and self-protection. As the sixteenth-century dramatist Thomas Nashe rather chillingly said: 'Beauty is but a flower Which wrinkles will devour.' This is what we're all scared of. My most-hated wrinkle, in the middle of my forehead, feels like it's doing just that: devouring my face. It has two little helper wrinkles either side of it, and together they plan to take over my face.

Rupert is always complaining about the amount of money I spend on creams. He says the women in our local perfumery treat me like a long-lost relative every time I walk in.

'You can hear the cheers across town,' he says. 'Probably because they know once you've been in they can shut up shop for the rest of the day.'

When everything's said and done, I'm as much of

a sucker in the pursuit of that ageless dream as the next woman. Despite knowing all that I do after my anti-ageing journey. I admit that I can't resist nice creams, and by nice I mean more expensive ones. Even if expensive creams don't really do any more for your skin than cheaper ones, I still prefer them. I tested several cheaper ranges for this book and although this may just be me, the products seemed cheap, they didn't smell as good and I didn't enjoy using them. They just felt like they wouldn't do me any good and I'm sure the placebo effect is big when it comes to creams. If a cream makes you feel good, chances are you will look good.

Buying a new cream that costs more than a pair of shoes is therapeutic, every time you use it. You open it and take the plastic bit off under the lid, making sure you take any cream off it before you throw it away. When you smooth it on your face you do so with care. You enjoy the texture, the smell, the look of your skin immediately after. This cream may not be any more effective than its cheaper cousin, but it feels like it is, and, rather like the placebo effect, that makes a difference.

After about fifteen minutes Alexandra comes back in. She removes my face pack and then goes through the routine she has worked out for me. It starts with the La

Prairie Essence of Skin Caviar Eye Complex, then the Cellular Radiance Eye Cream. This is followed by face serum, then face cream. For the body she has picked the Emulsion Caviar Corps followed by the Caviar Corps. She rubs a bit on my shoulders and chest. It feels silky and smells divine. This cream, she tells me, will be especially effective on those nasty wrinkles between my breasts which I can see are just itching to get out. All this needs to be administered morning and evening. How on earth will I find the time?

Alexandra turns on the light and proudly shows me my face. I am glowing. Miraculously my skin seems tighter, my eyes seem wider and more awake (though possibly in part due to my kip during the massage). What is incredible is that the flappy skin that used to be on my eyelids is stretched and taut. How has this happened?

I do look greasy, but my complexion is flawless. Alexandra has a point. So, how much will all this cost me?

This is where those of a sensitive disposition should look away.

The night cream alone is £120. Someone at La Prairie is making a lot of money while other people sleep. The Caviar body cream I have grown so fond of is a snip at £250 and the day cream a mere £75. The face pack is £90, and for ten eye patches I will have to pay another £90. I think I'll stick to cucumber.

I look at Alexandra in horror. She points out that everything lasts at least three months. For those prices they should last ten years. If I buy everything she suggests I will leave the Ritz having spent over £1,000. It's just not an option.

'Well, then I think you should maybe just take the eye creams as that is the most urgent, and do the rest when you can,' she suggests. 'I'll give you some testers to be going along with.'

As I lean on the reception desk trying to divide my afternoon's fun onto several credit cards while the other Alexandra charmingly tells me it doesn't matter that they keep bouncing and to remember that they're open from 9 a.m. to 9 p.m. seven days a week, I reflect that the first thing you need to avoid ageing is buckets of cash.

CHAPTER FOUR

A Cheaper Option

So far in my anti-ageing quest I have been to an exclusive clinic on the shores of Lake Geneva and the Ritz Hotel in Paris. This is all going swimmingly. On my way home, I call Carla to tell her I feel extremely young and pleased with myself.

'So you should do,' she shrieks. 'What you've just done costs more than the annual GDP of most small African countries. If you're not looking seventeen, you should ask for your money back. How about writing about something the rest of us can do, preferably in the comfort of our own homes?'

She's right, of course. I can't spend my life travelling to exclusive clinics. I have neither the time nor the money. And I am still not ready to try more drastic anti-ageing methods like Botox or a chemical peel. There has to be another option. I decide to try to recreate my Ritz experience at home.

Finding a good time to do this between work and bringing up three small children is not easy but my opportunity comes when we are woken up one day at 5.30 a.m. by a farmer spraying the fields.

'And on the morning of the World Cup Final,' says Rupert furiously, getting up to go for a bike ride.

I start with the cleansing. Since my trip to Geneva and Paris I have been taking much better care of myself. I have been cleansing every morning and night, moisturising my face and body and wearing sunscreen. My skin looks good. *The* wrinkle is still there, but I don't expect miracles. I am already feeling more positive about this ageing lark. The sun salutes are going well (as long as I can do them before my son wakes up as he thinks I am pretending to be a climbing frame) and I carry a bottle of water around with me at all times.

I have also been reading up about the benefits of facials. Apparently they are an essential step to young-looking skin. They thoroughly cleanse your face as well as removing the top dead layers of skin, thereby encouraging cell renewal. They should be carried out at least once a month, according to a website called www.beauticiansonnet.com, confirming what Alexandra told me, and by a professional with at least 300 hours' training.

I have no formal training, but how hard can removing a few dead cells be?

After cleansing with a Chanel wash-off cleanser I start to exfoliate. Alexandra at the Ritz told me to exfoliate once a week. It removes the top layer of the skin, encouraging newer, younger cells to surface. I am already beginning to feel better when I administer my Anti-ageing Concept 1 Global Beauty Exfoliating Mask. This is something I bought about a year ago in a rush of enthusiasm at Harvey Nichols Beyond Beauty and haven't had time to use since. I lie on my bed and wait for it to take effect. The instructions tell me I need to leave it on for twenty-five minutes. Then I hear the first voice.

'Mum-my!' It's my son. He has got up and wandered into the kitchen. I find him there with a half-eaten fresh fig.

'Not good,' he tells me as he pushes it into my hand. I think briefly about smearing it on my face – people make face packs from stranger substances – but instead I throw it away. I take him into my room and install him on my bed with his tractor.

By now I am beginning to feel like I have tarmac

drying on my face. I am itching to get this thing off and it's only been on for four minutes.

'Mummy, there's an animal in my room.' My younger daughter is the next one to wake up. She approaches my bed and looks a little perplexed.

'Mummy, you don't look at all normal,' she says. I explain to her that this was all her godmother Carla's idea and she should blame her. But Bea soon loses interest. She is more concerned with what she calls a 'hopper-grass' on her shelf.

We remove the creature and go back towards my bedroom via the bathroom mirror. Bea is right, I don't look at all normal. In fact I look like I imagine I will look aged ninety. It's horrible. The mask has dried on my face creating wrinkles everywhere.

I peer even closer in the mirror. My complexion looks dry and flaky. I hate myself. If this is what I'll look like when I get old, I'm not going there.

Olivia, my elder daughter, walks into the bathroom. 'Mummy, you look like a monster,' she says, before helpfully adding, 'Maybe it won't come off at all.'

She has a point. The wind could change and I could be stuck like this for ever, looking like the witch in *The Wizard of Oz*. This is not a risk I'm prepared to take. I rinse the mask off, not without a little difficulty as the bloody thing has grown attached to me. Suddenly I feel free.

'I'm now going to stick my head over a bowl of hot water,' I announce with renewed enthusiasm.

'Oh,' says Bea.

'Why are you doing this?' asks Olivia.

'Carla told her to,' says Bea.

'Donkey,' says Leonardo.

They have been promised donkey rides at the local fair. As it is still before seven I explain that the donkeys are asleep but that we'll go after breakfast. Thankfully Eli, our au pair, is now up so I install the children on the terrace with toast and honey before continuing my treatment.

I sit at the kitchen table with a towel over my head breathing in steam. It's not exactly the same as lying on a bed at the Ritz with steam being gently sprayed in my general direction, listening to soothing if faintly naff music. I would say the effect is a little more violent as I am closer to the steam and instead of relaxing music I am listening to children running around the kitchen table arguing.

'Don't kick me or I'll kick you,' screeches Olivia.

'You're evil,' says Leo.

'There's a bee outside who wants to eat my honey,' wails Bea.

'Anyone who wants to go on a donkey ride goes and sits down this minute, understood?' I yell from my steam dungeon. 'Eli, can you tell me when ten minutes are up, please?'

The children behave better after that and I am left to enjoy my steaming. Actually it's not very enjoyable, it's very hot. It is July and we are in the midst of a heat wave so even at this early hour it's boiling. Still, I am enjoying the idea of my pores opening up and all the dirt coming out.

'How much longer to go?' I ask Eli.

'Seven minutes,' she replies. I can't believe it. Are they on different time in Slovakia? She can't be right.

'Are you sure, Eli?'

'Yes,' she replies.

What am I supposed to do for seven minutes with a towel over my head? I try to use the time to relax and plan my next step. This involves squeezing blackheads; there's something to look forward to.

'Can I see you?' Leo is at my side, tugging at the towel. I lift the towel. 'Ugh,' he says and runs off

'Five more minutes,' says Eli.

Finally it's time to go and squeeze my blackheads. I have read that you're meant to use tissue paper on your fingertips so as not to damage your skin but I just can't get a grip with bits of paper flapping around and so I just dig in. Rather satisfyingly three blackheads surrender.

Now it's time for the Roc Moisturising Anti-Fatigue Mask that promises to boost radiance and visibly smooth my skin. It is in the form of a sodden piece of cloth with holes cut out for your eyes, nose and mouth. Rather horrifyingly, it reminds me of the image of the woman covered in a mask being helped by a young man, which was all over the papers after the London bombings in 2005.

I put some Liz Earle Instant Boost Skin Tonic on two cotton wool pads for my eyes and prepare to lie down for fifteen minutes to let the goodness soak through into my opened pores.

Bea takes this moment of stillness as a rare opportunity to come and lie on top of me. This, of course, incenses her sister, who comes to annoy her. From under my mask I issue the threat of cancelling the donkey ride again. Useful things, donkeys.

I almost doze off, as does Bea, but finally my treatment is over. I take off the mask and the eye pads, and rub any excess moisture into my skin as instructed. I take a look in the mirror. My skin does look smooth and much brighter than when I started. My eyes look wider and more awake, although I still look (and feel) as if I have been up half the night.

It was not as relaxing an experience as the Ritz but whereas that set me back £100, this little episode has probably cost me £5, if that.

'Eli, does my skin look any different?' I ask her as she passes my bathroom.

She stares at me for a moment. 'I don't know,' she says. 'But I like your top.'

One worrying side effect of my home-grown facial is that a spot develops on my cheek. I know you're meant to leave spots alone, but that's just not part of my genetic make-up. So the spot and I battle for supremacy for three days, just before I have to go to Paris and be photographed for a story for the *Daily Telegraph*. Of course the spot wins, but luckily the story is spiked so said spot doesn't achieve international fame. Which was clearly its evil plan.

Another anti-ageing technique you can try at home is the facial workout. This basically involves pulling silly faces, so could be quite good fun. Tina Richards is mad about a daily facial workout with an electro-stimulator called the Tua Viso. This is a machine that stimulates your facial muscles, boosts collagen production and improves the skin's microcirculation, oxygenation and lymphatic drainage. The manufacturers say that if you incorporate using Tua Viso into your lifestyle you will prevent the need for a face-lift. Tina swears by it.

'I think it's brilliant,' she says. 'If you use it, it really works. You just have to bother. Once you get into it, it's really therapeutic. Electro-stimulation of facial muscles makes logical sense to me. Also, I've met the Italian clinical dermatologist a few times who supervised the independent clinical trial at Bologna University, and discussed the clinical research on the product – the evidence is statistically significant.'

I tried the Tua Viso. It is a hand-held gadget with two electrodes that you wet with water and use to stimulate certain muscles on your face. At the beginning you're meant to do it once a day, Tina has now 'graduated' to three times a week. I had it for about two months before I even had the time to try it. Then I finally got it out of its packaging and went to work.

The idea is to place the electrodes on certain parts of your face in order actually to see what it does. I followed the instructions for position one. Nothing happened so I increased the electrical current. I got one hell of a surprise; my whole eyebrow lifted about two centimetres. I looked like a lunatic. When I moved down to the mouth area I looked like a goldfish on heat.

At one stage Rupert caught sight of me and thought I'd finally lost the plot. 'What the hell are you doing now?' he yelled.

'I'm exercising my facial muscles, to make the wrinkles go away.'

'You can have as many wrinkles as you like, no one will talk to you anyway if you wander around looking like a mad woman with an electrical gadget stuck to her face,' he said before wandering off, leaving me to it.

Once I had understood how to control the current it was not an uncomfortable sensation. Actually after I had a consultation with Tina and understood how to use the gadget properly it was quite a nice feeling. I watched the muscles on my face contort into strange shapes and imagined all the good I was doing and how young I would look and how I would never have to have a face-lift and look like a cat in a tunnel, as a friend of mine puts it. This lasted for about three days. Then I just couldn't find the time to do the exercises, partly because I believed you're meant to do them without make-up on. For me that's either first thing in the morning (no hope with the children to get to school) or last thing at night (no hope, just about manage to read two paragraphs of

Elle mag or *Private Eye* before I pass out). Also I had been instructed that you are meant to do it with your elbows resting on a surface, which means you have to sit still, not something I can do unless I am at my desk working.

I'm sure the Tua Viso is brilliant. Tina looks very good on it, by the way. She has the best skin I have seen on anyone that hasn't been airbrushed, and has not got a single wrinkle. But it is, as she says, a commitment. If you are going to invest in one (and they're not expensive) then do go to one of the training sessions Tina runs. I think that would make all the difference.

Tua Viso reminded me a bit of the BRAVA breast enlargement system, which is meant to make your tits bigger but you have to wander around for six months with a cylinder on each breast for at least ten hours a day. Now I am prepared to do almost anything (cheat, lie, steal, sell my children) to have bigger breasts, but not that.

One alternative to the Tua Viso comes from Carolyn, a lady who lives in Seattle. She owns a company called Carolyn's Facial Fitness (www.carolynsfacialfitness.com) and teaches people to retain a youthful look by exercising their facial muscles. 'It's so much fun looking younger as I grow older and knowing it's all natural,' says Carolyn. She first came across the idea of facial fitness when she turned fifty. Her mother had her first face-lift when she was forty-eight years old. Within five years she needed 'more work', as Carolyn puts it.

'By the time she was fifty she looked permanently surprised,' says Carolyn. 'By the time she was sixty she started looking distorted. She was not ageing gracefully at all and I thought, there just has to be an alternative to this disaster.'

Carolyn does not believe in Botox. She works with a cosmetic surgeon who has been horrified at the number of women who come to his clinic suffering from the adverse effects of it. 'Many of them have been using Botox for so long their muscles have atrophied beyond recovery,' she says. 'So, I turned to other methods of preventing the sagging, bagging and wrinkles that were coming to live with me, especially on my face and neck. At age fifty-two I was really looking older than my years. I had lost a lot of weight, which was part of the problem. That was when I started my quest to at least look my age and not older.'

Carolyn came across a book published in 1907 by Sanford Bennett, known as 'The man who grew young at seventy'. In *Old Age, Its Cause and Prevention* Bennett mentions a woman, Ninon de L'Enclos 'The woman who never grew old', born in Paris on 15 May 1616. She was supposed to have been doing facial exercises to 'keep' her youth. In the book he describes a technique he calls rubbing out wrinkles, which Carolyn has incorporated into her programme. It consists of holding wrinkles between your forefinger and index finger in a V-sign and literally rubbing the wrinkle away.

Carolyn's programme works on the principle of regaining the fresh, firm, natural look of youth. It contours and lifts the face and the neck. 'It is based on muscle resistance training that not only builds muscle fibre to create a lift but isometrics as well to enhance and tone the skin,' says Carolyn. 'I consulted a medical doctor and a professor of anatomy and physiology when designing my programme so I would not only address all fifty-seven muscles of the face and neck, but ensure it was safe, dynamic and thorough. I was able to design a complete workout that was no more than fifteen minutes long and would still give me the results I wanted. I just knew I wouldn't devote more than fifteen minutes a session to my face and neck.'

I see a picture of Carolyn on her website and think she looks great but of course I can't take that as evidence that her programme works; she could have been using that same picture for the past forty years.

This is a well-known anti-ageing trick used by newspaper columnists the world over (and one I am not adverse to). Next to their by-line you invariably see a picture taken in the 1970s.

Luckily I have a friend in Seattle who has founded a group called GOG or Growing Old Gracefully. Peggy, who is in her fifties, immediately orders Carolyn's facial fitness kit and tells me she is going to go for a consultation with the lady herself as she doesn't 'want to end up looking like Jim Carrey'.

Peggy's first impression of Carolyn is extremely positive. 'Carolyn's face looks marvellous, and not in that stretched-tight-as-a-drum way that you get from a face-lift,' she says. 'She doesn't try and dress young, and has a kind of timeless quality about her.' The workshop is interesting. She sends me a funny email about the session.

Carolyn looks good and is also very lively and energetic. It's wonderful to see someone her age whose face and body move so freely. And she doesn't try to act or dress young, which is also refreshing. She looks a little bit like a druid and I mean that as a compliment.

I am learning the routine and it is HARD. Once I have it down pat, I apparently need to spend 'only' fifteen minutes a day. I know I will stick with it, but I suspect the limitation to this kind of programme is that most women would prefer two hours under the knife and two weeks in hiding to the day-to-day discipline that facial fitness requires. However, I think it can produce visible results. And judging from Carolyn's face, it gives you a face that is natural and that leaves you free to express emotions through facial expressions – what a concept! Some of the exercises are so funny – like doing push-ups with your cheeks and pulling your eyelids down while holding your brow up. Neck exercises are also included (ever notice how face-lifts can accentuate the age of the neck? ewwww!).

Facial fitness has its detractors. Some say that using facial muscles actually increase wrinkles and that we're better off with Botox. Those of the holistic school like Carolyn would argue that paralysing the facial muscles via injections leads to muscle atrophy and possibly bone damage, because the facial muscles are directly connected to the underlying bones.

Peggy, my GOG friend, agrees with this. 'I have seen the findings of recent scientific work on the long-term effects of Botox, done by disinterested scientists who are not working for dermatologists, plastic surgeons or pharmaceutical companies, and it appears that paralysing the facial muscles can do serious long-term damage,' she says.

I haven't tried it out, but Carolyn's method sounds fairly good to me. I think it stands to reason that if you exercise your muscles they will be in better shape. And no one has ever suggested exercising from the neck down is a bad thing; that it creates wrinkles, fine lines and sagging skin. The consensus is that exercise is by far the best way to achieve and maintain a firm body as we age. Why should it be any different for the face and neck? In addition, Botox cannot help with sagging skin. So maybe there's room for a bit of both?

'The crux of the matter is – what is more appealing to you? Facial exercise or the surgeon's knife?' says Peggy. 'Facial exercising is a much less invasive way of reducing the sagging that comes with age.'

But what of the woman herself? Surely proof of the efficacy of her programme must start with her? 'Carolyn looks fabulous,' Peggy tells me. 'She has some fine lines but no deep wrinkles, and her face is nicely built up in a natural way, rather than being pulled tight. What's more, she has the freedom of movement in her face and neck that surgery survivors and Botox devotees lack. She is lovely in a full and rounded way (by which I don't mean fat) a living demonstration that facial fitness does not cause wrinkles.'

Peggy is also delighted with the results she has seen on herself. 'I have found that by bringing blood and oxygen flow to the face, facial exercises improve the skin as well as the sagginess and the wrinkles,' says Peggy. 'When I first started, I got some pimples and this worried me. I think it was trapped toxins being liberated. They cleared up quickly and my skin looks better, the colour is more even and my skin is smoother and less dry than it has been for ages.'

After two months of doing the programme Peggy travelled back to Paris where she has lived for many years. 'Every one of my friends noted that I looked refreshed, younger, less tired,' she says. 'They all attributed this to the fact I am happy and well cared for by a wonderful man now. [Peggy recently got married.] Little do they suspect that my "refreshed" look comes from pulling on various parts of my face for fifteen minutes every day. The most spectacular change is around the eyes. In recent years, my eyes have been puffy when I wake up, sometimes taking hours to return to a semi-normal state. Now they are puffy when I wake up, but less so, and the puffiness is vastly reduced by the eye exercises. I can see it happening before my eyes, so to speak. Freaky!'

Six months later she is still going strong.

I continue to manage four or five facial workouts a week and I am here to tell you the results are there, *she writes.* I had dinner with a friend last week and she said marriage must be working for me because I look ten years younger, and she really couldn't quite put her finger on it, but I looked radiant, what kind of miracle cream was I using, etc. I told her I was using my fingers and facial muscles plus sunscreen. The best thing about these exercises is they exfoliate your skin. Fabulous to see the little flakes floating off as you rub instead of becoming patches of dry skin.

From the women I have spoken to I am convinced that programmes like Carolyn's Facial Fitness and the Tua Viso do some good. But they do require a commitment. Of course it is quicker and easier to nip into your dermatologist's for some Botox and fillers. Rather like having liposuction instead of exercising to get rid of unwanted fat. The question is, which would you rather do? And what can you afford? And do you believe the long-term benefits of a system like Carolyn's outweigh the convenience of a quick-fix Botox injection?

Carolyn sent me her kit and I sat and looked at it for weeks. Then I opened it and was slightly overwhelmed by all the information I had to take in. I took it away with me on holiday to give it my full attention. But the children needed more attention than my wrinkles and so it stayed in the packet. And it has stayed there ever since. I have no doubt it has its benefits and it seems to work for Peggy. But much as I love the idea of rubbing out *the* most hated wrinkle, I think to win this particular battle I may need something a little stronger, and a little more immediate.

CHAPTER FIVE

Environmental Ageing

There is nothing quite like a children's birthday party to put me in a lousy mood. First there is all the preparation. Then there is the sight of all those awful things I don't want them to eat but which seem to be obligatory on birthdays, and finally the children. Parents show up bang on time, dump the kids and run. You never know if or when you're going to see them again.

Since I met Mary, though, birthday parties have become bearable. Mary lives in the same village as we do and has four children. Rather conveniently, her three older ones and my three of the equivalent age are all best friends. Poor little Valentine, who is two, has no one, but I'm not prepared to risk stretch marks just so she can have a playmate. Mary is too nice to leave me with all four of her children, so she stays with me and we entertain everyone together.

At Bea's last birthday party, Mary and I are busy organising the pass-the-parcel when one of Bea's friends shows up with her mother and her grandmother.

'I heard you were writing a book about ageing so I bought my mother along,' says Bea's friend's mother. 'Everyone is always telling her how amazing she is.'

The grandmother wafts in looking like Lauren Bacall. She is American so even has the right accent. She moves with ease, her skin is clear, her hair thick and well cut. She is elegantly dressed in pale green trousers and a cream silk shirt. Her green eyes are sparkling. She is slim. I guess she is about sixty. Turns out she is ninety.

'What is your secret?' is my first question.

'I have significantly reduced the environmental ageing factors that affect us,' she tells me.

'The what?' I ask. I have no idea what an environmental ageing factor is. Apparently they are everything that ages you bar your genes. So everything from sun damage to bad diet. According to the guru Tina Richards, environmental factors can account for up to 80 per cent of skin ageing.

The vision smiles patiently. 'Forty years ago I cut

out sugar, wheat and alcohol from my diet completely. I drink heaps of water and I exercise every day. I wear sunscreen all the time but never sit in the sun.'

'Doesn't that get a bit dull?' I ask her, rather unsure of what I can offer her to drink or whether she might need a parasol to shade her from any sun on my terrace.

'Well, it did, but then I started to feel so good on it that I realised it was worth it,' she says, smiling benignly.

'But surely sometimes a bit of sugar slips past?' Mary asks incredulously.

'Not if I can help it,' she says in a light-hearted tone that makes me want to strangle her.

'What if you're at a party and everything on offer has something you don't eat in it?' I ask.

'There are always vegetables or some fruit; I carry some nuts and rye bread around for emergencies.'

Mary and I are astounded. This woman is a walking miracle. Is she for real? Maybe she is an alien that has been put on earth to make us all feel impossibly inadequate? She's certainly doing a great job.

'Your hair is such a lovely colour,' I say, searching surreptitiously for face-lift scars on her scalp.

'Thank you.' She beams. 'I decided to go for the grey/blonde look a few years ago. I think it's essential to age gracefully, too many people dye their hair badly.'

'What can I get you to drink?' I ask her.

'Just some water, please,' she responds.

'Sparkling?'

'Oh, no, dear, just plain,' she says, shaking her head. 'Sparkling is not good for one's digestion. Although I will sometimes allow myself a small glass of champagne.'

I remember a story about the writer Karen Blixen, who went to New York in 1959, towards the end of her life. She had lunch with the playwright Arthur Miller and Marilyn Monroe. Blixen was seventy-four by then. She insisted on eating only oysters and drinking champagne.

'Did your doctor suggest this diet?' Miller asked her.

'My doctors are appalled by my diet,' she responded. 'But I love oysters and champagne, and they love me.'

Sadly, my guest has only a liking for champagne in common with Blixen. She is too pleased with herself for words. I am amazed she's lived this long, despite her po-faced ways.

You've guessed it. Mary and I are by now beginning to loathe this woman, I suppose in part because she makes us feel like such failures. There is more sugar on the table than she has eaten in the last forty years. We certainly drunk more alcohol the night before than she has since she was pre-menopausal.

'It's all very well,' Mary whispers to me, 'but I bet she doesn't have many children.'

Yes, that was obviously it, I think smugly. It's all very easy to age with grace when you haven't given birth several times and been kept awake at night for years on end.

'Do you have many children?' I ask her innocently.

'Oh, yes,' she responds serenely. 'I have ten.'

We look at each other in horror. Thankfully we are called away to deal with a child who has decided to push his sister in the pool fully clothed. I have to admit to Mary that I am tempted to do the same to our illustrious guest.

'Oh, me too,' she says. 'I feel like eating a Crunchie in front of her. How can you be that bloody good? It's just not human.'

'She is beyond dull,' I say. 'Remind me never to become so holier-than-thou. Or if I do, push me in the pool.'

But however dull she was, this lady was right about one thing: the environmental element of ageing is the part we can actually do something about. The impact of genetic versus environmental ageing depends on a person's behaviour. If you have pro-ageing genetic make-up but you consistently take good care of yourself, you could age the same, if not better, than someone who has anti-ageing genetics but lives a pro-ageing lifestyle. In my view whatever you can do to slow down environmental ageing is worth a try.

So why does the skin age? Rather depressingly the intrinsic or internal/genetic ageing has already begun by our mid-twenties, although it doesn't show in most people until a few years later. Collagen production slows down, elastin is less effective and the turnover of dead skin cells decreases. Intrinsic ageing manifests itself in various ways such as fine wrinkles, loss of underlying fat in the face, grey hair and hair loss. Extrinsic or external ageing, like the sun, smoke, stress, alcohol and so on, does the rest.

Almost everyone I interviewed for this book said that 90 per cent of environmental ageing is caused by the sun. Repeated sun exposure not only attacks but also impairs production of new collagen and elastin. Just a few minutes of exposure a day will significantly age your skin. But the irritating thing is, when you're brown you look so much healthier and, well, younger. And there's nothing quite as relaxing as sitting in the sun. Even though I now live in the south of France I still seek out the sun, which I think every person that grew up in England automatically does. I hear my mother's voice saying, 'Get outside, it's a sunny day,' even though here we have about 300 sunny days a year. If I go to a lunch outside I always sit facing the sun; I just love the feel of it. If I am going to age well I will have to break this habit.

It had never occurred to me to wear sunblock on a daily basis until I started working on this book. Apparently you should even wear it all year round, even in England, where the sun rarely makes an appearance.

'The sun is your worst enemy,' says Tina Richards. 'So the most important thing you can do for your skin is to protect it.'

This doesn't just mean slapping on a bit of sunscreen as you head to the beach. Sunscreen must be worn every day of the year, on your face, neck, décolletage, the area below and around your neckline, and hands. Elle Macpherson says that every morning she brushes her teeth and then puts on her sunscreen. Let's hope she doesn't mix up the tubes. And how good does she look, aged forty-something?

Tina says that the more fastidious you are about protecting yourself from the sun the more you will delay ageing. 'Put your sunblock on before you draw the curtains in the morning if it's sunny outside because UVA passes through glass,' she says. 'Don't go out for two minutes to hang the washing on the line without first putting on sunblock. And sunblock should go all over your face including around your eye area, and up your neck including the sides right up behind your ears, and remember to put it on the back of your hands.'

Obviously if you are heading to the beach wearing just a thong you need some on the rest of your body too. And you can get tanned in the shade, so there's no need to fry your skin. I have tried to take Tina's advice and put sunblock behind my ears but I just feel too silly. And it makes my hair greasy. But I never go out without sunblock on my face and I slap masses on the-most-hated-wrinkle between my eyebrows. My reasoning is that if I overprotect it, the rest of my face might catch up at some stage and it will not stand out so badly.

The sunscreen you choose needs to protect you from both UVA and UVB rays; you need a so-called 'high-factor broad-spectrum sunblock'. Tina explains the distinction. 'UVA is referred to as "A" for ageing, and UVB as "B" for burning in various literature, but the letters were originally devised simply to distinguish the different wavelengths of ultraviolet light,' she says. 'However, it just so happens that UVA, which has the longer wavelength and isn't absorbed by the earth's ozone layer, is mostly responsible for skin ageing. It is equally present on a dull winter's day as at midday on a sunny day in August. UVB, which causes the burning of the skin and turns your skin lobster pink, varies in level according to the time of day and year.'

Dr David Orentreich, a New York dermatologist, really freaked me out when I went to interview him by showing me the effects of the sun on myself.

'Look at that piece of skin underneath your chin,' he said handing me a mirror. 'It has had the same treatment in everything as the rest of your skin; it has the same diet, the same creams, the same amount of sleep and so on. The only difference is that it is not exposed to the sun.'

The patch of skin he was talking about looks younger, firmer and smoother than the rest of me. It looks like it belongs to a different person, a Daisy Buchanan-type character with perfectly creamy translucent skin and manicured nails.

Sun damage starts at an early age. I have a friend who was brought up in Zimbabwe. She is now in her fifties and when she was a child people didn't bother with sunscreens. She has been plagued with skin cancer her whole adult life.

Cosmetic signs of sun damage include sun spots, also known as 'souvenirs of Florida' in America, for obvious reasons, or liver spots. The technical term is solar lentigos. These start off as brown spots or freckles, mainly on the backs of our hands, our chest and face but can deteriorate into mottled darker patches that are horribly ageing. Sun damage can now be treated by dermatologists, mainly through skin-resurfacing (peels) or lasers or IPL treatments. You can also treat it at home with vitamin C-based products that are good for repairing sun-damaged skin. Tina recommends retinol-based (vitamin A derivatives that encourage cell growth) products or a prescription retinol cream to treat solar damage. The latter is quite a strong treatment and if you do go to see a dermatologist to get some, then you should start slowly with small amounts. In fact one thing you can do is to get your skin used to it by starting off with a non-prescription retinol cream like the Philosophy one I use.

Is there a viable alternative to a real tan? Not really, no. I have tried every fake tan there is. Most of them are dreadful and have that really obvious fake tan smell. Among the better ones are the Clarins self-tanning milk with sun protection (although it does still have that fake tan smell) and the Rodial Brazilian Tan (less smelly). The Garnier Ambre No-Streaks Bronzer Light Self-Tanning spray is also good. Another method is to soak cotton wool pads in strong tea and then wipe your face and body with them. This is an old French trick I came across through a friend whose mother used to do it. I have yet to try it; somehow the thought of covering myself in cold tea is not that attractive. Tanning beds are naturally out of the question: they emit UVA rays. Tina calls them 'ageing machines'.

The second most damaging thing for your skin after the sun is smoking. You should not only never smoke yourself but also avoid second-hand smoke.

'Every puff of cigarette smoke is bristling with free radicals – that is, highly reactive fragmented oxygen molecules,' says Tina. 'It really is extremely damaging to your skin as well as your lungs.'

Dr Patrick Bowler, who runs the Court House Clinic in London, agrees. 'Smoking has a very specific effect on the skin,' he says. 'It helps to break down collagen, thereby damaging the skin's collagen, which makes the skin less elastic and looser. Also, smokers are pale and grey because the nicotine makes the blood vessels clamp down so there's not enough blood flowing to the skin.'

Smoking destroys the ability of the skin to regenerate, and regeneration is, of course, what makes skin look younger. It also gives you those unsightly wrinkles around your mouth that you get from pursing your lips and puffing. If you do smoke then do this: find a picture of the poet W. H. Auden a few years before he died. A wrinklier, less healthy-looking image is hard to find. Auden was a heavy smoker. Cut out the picture and every time you feel like a cigarette, take a look at it. If that doesn't put you off, nothing will. And smoking doesn't only affect the way you look; it actually affects the way your DNA ages. Researchers have found that key parts of a smoker's DNA are on average almost five years older than those of a non-smoker. So you are biologically ageing as well as wrecking your looks.

Aside from avoiding sun and smoking, Dr Bowler agrees with Tina that your daily skin-care routine is the key. I never used to bother with cleansing at all. Then I started researching this book and discovered a whole new world of yummy creams, lotions and potions. I now have at least one cream for every part of my body. Last time Carla came to stay she went into my bathroom and came out with her head in her hands.

'Please tell me these creams aren't all yours,' she wailed.

They are. And I love them. There isn't a single one I want to do without. I have become addicted to my daily skin-care regime in the way some people become addicted to jogging. It has almost become a form of meditation. In the morning and evening I spend about ten minutes in the bathroom looking after my body and face. Whatever else is going on, I make the time to slap endless creams on. In fact I begin even before creams, with body brushing. This is a brilliant thing that makes you tingle all over and gets rid of dead cells; it is exfoliating and also stimulates the lymphatic system and microcirculation. Then I start rubbing myself with creams. Now that I live in France, of course, I use an anti-cellulite cream. I am always amazed when spring comes; the window displays in all the pharmacies in France are suddenly filled with creams that promise to take inches off your thighs and make you a cellulite-free zone.

'They can't possibly work, can they?' I asked my French friend Alexandra once as we were passing my local chemist.

'You're so English,' she said, looking at me with disdain.

If they're good enough for your average (thin, cellulite-free) French woman, they're good enough for me. Perfect Slim by L'Oréal has come out well in clinical trials but personally I prefer the Clarins Lift Minceur, which I sometimes mix with their Huile Tonic body oil – heavenly. So the anti-cellulite cream takes care of the hips and thighs. For the lower legs I use a heavy moisturiser or baby oil as my skin there is almost always a bit flaky. On my arms and tummy I often use Nivea or, if I'm going out, a sumptuous cream that makes you glow called Glow Lotion by Soap and Glory. The breasts are a big issue. Well, not big in that sense, but there are so many products to choose from. Most of the time I use either Clarins or Decléor. The Clarins ones (Clarins Bust Beauty Gel which smells amazing and the Clarins Bust Beauty Lotion) are both lovely but I found the Decléor Perfect Bust toning mousse is the most effective.

I vary the creams I use on my face but I now always bring the cream down to the décolletage area as well. This is such a sensitive part of your body and ages so badly it's worth remembering it every day. Put sunscreen on it too. I always use a serum on my face, sometimes mixed with a vitamin C powder, as well as sunscreen and a moisturiser to finish off. This use of vitamin C is what the dermatological companies confusingly call 'topical'. This just means putting it on your face. You should do this in the morning (or use another antioxidant) and use a retinol cream at night, something like the Philosophy one I mentioned earlier or the SkinCeuticals Retinol 0.3, but you must then use a sunblock during the day.

I exfoliate my face three times a week and really if you do that there isn't that much of a need to go for facials or microdermabrasions. So you can save yourself a fortune there. Although there's nothing quite as relaxing as sleeping through a facial.

Part of anti-ageing has got to be grooming. If your skin is shining and your nails are painted then you're going to look better than if you've just dragged yourself out of bed into the nearest pair of leggings. But if you eat and drink all the wrong things then you may as well just put margarine on your face. Nutrition is something I cover in more detail later on in the book; just a quick word on alcohol now. According to Dr Bowler, excessive drinking is out for those of us who want to stay looking good.

'A couple of glasses of wine are OK, but you know how bad you look after a night of drinking,' he says. 'If you drink all the time it will have an effect on how you look.'

This drinking thing is something I find tough. The problem is a little bit of alcohol is actually good for you. So there's the excuse to get started with a small glass of red wine. Then you have a nice time and after two glasses you forget about the hangover. Or as my husband, Rupert, puts it: 'I feel so great after two glasses I tell myself I'll feel twice as good after four.'

But you only have to look at an alcoholic to see how much damage drinking can do to your skin. Think of those broken veins, that red nose look, the saggy skin. Think about how rough you look on a hangover. And how rough you feel, come to think of it.

Carla and I have a friend, let's call her Miranda, who I always thought was incredibly grumpy, bordering on depressed. Turns out she's not grumpy, she's just permanently hung over.

'Is Miranda a big drinker?' I asked Carla when she told me this.

'Is Miranda a big drinker?' she responded, looking at me incredulously. 'Does Dolly Parton sleep on her back?'

Of course you can live to be one hundred if you give up all the things that make you want to live to one hundred, alcohol being one of them. My father-in-law is a classic example of this. He was told about seven years ago that he should give up drinking alcohol. At the time he was seventy-five. He stopped for a while but after a few months decided that actually he missed his wine and his cognac so much that, if denying himself a drink meant he would live longer he simply wasn't interested. I think it's a good attitude. I am not coming round to Carla's 'live fast, die young and have a beautiful corpse' way of thinking – although according to Rupert it's too late for her anyway – but at seventy-five, if you want to have a glass of wine then why the hell not? I am happy to say he is now eighty-two and still going strong. In fact, he's a great example of how a positive attitude can keep you young. He enjoys every day, never moans, and eats and drinks exactly what he wants. The other extraordinary thing is he never drinks water.

When I interviewed Inès de la Fressange, the original supermodel and Chanel muse, she told me her top anti-ageing tip was sleep. Sleep deprivation is, I am convinced, lethal in ageing terms. When we sleep our cells regenerate. We also remove toxins when we sleep, and activate immune system cells. The reason it is called 'beauty sleep' is that our rate of cell renewal is at its highest when we sleep, so we wake up looking refreshed. As I heard from the yogi in Switzerland, sleep is an essential anti-ageing tool and I often think that one of the major benefits of beauty treatments is falling asleep.

But of course it isn't just a question of sleeping any old way you like. No, you have to make sure you sleep on your back, otherwise you could be creating wrinkles as you snore. What a terrible thought.

According to Melanie Vasseur from Vasseur Scientific Skincare, a San Diego-based skincare company, 'Sleeping on your side is the second cause of wrinkles after the sun, because when you sleep on your side you are ironing in wrinkles on your skin. This means that on average, you are spending over 2,500 hours per year reversing the positive effects of your skincare treatments just in your sleep.'

This sleeping-wrinkle-thing is a nightmare for me. I sleep badly almost all the time. And I sleep better on my side. But now when I wake up at three o'clock in the morning worrying about whether my children will die horribly in some car crash or if I remembered to feed the cat, I also have to worry about whether it is more ageing to not sleep or to fall back to sleep on my side. And it's not only your face you need to worry about – sleeping on your side can cause wrinkles in the décolletage area as well. I'm somewhat comforted by the fact that I am not the first woman to feel this stress. Diane de Poitiers, royal French mistress extraordinaire, slept sitting up in order to avoid wrinkles.

Once you're in the right position for a good night's sleep, this is how sleep helps your body fight ageing. For one thing, when we sleep the body produces the hormone melatonin, which helps fight free radicals. It has been suggested, for example, that reduced melatonin production may significantly contribute to higher cancer rates in night workers. In fact, during sleep, all your hormones rebalance so if you're menopausal don't do the night shift. Or if you do, then take a prolonged-release melatonin supplement. I find that when I don't get enough sleep I get very stressed, yet another terribly ageing factor beginning with S. Rather like smoking, stress speeds up ageing by harming your DNA. Also, the negative messages and chemicals your body releases when you get stressed directly age your skin and appearance. As Patrick Bowler says: 'Just look at how badly Tony Blair aged during his ten years in power.' An extreme example of this is a friend of mine whose son died in a car accident when he was only six. My friend, who was in his late thirties at the time, went grey literally overnight.

But stress does not only damage your looks. The expression 'sick with worry' is true. There is a clinically proven link between psychological stress and physical diseases. Stress ages you by releasing free radicals into your system, which in turn damage your cells and their ability to renew or function efficiently.

Reducing stress is essential. I find exercise really helps, which is in itself another effective way to reduce environmental ageing; so a double whammy of anti-ageing. In fact, exercise is the one thing, along with the sun, that everyone I interviewed for this book talked about. It is good for just about everything from your heart to your arteries to your immune system to your energy levels and your bone density. Strength building with weights can actually reverse ageing in muscles and also increase your human growth hormone production, something that declines as you age. My father once said that time spent exercising is never wasted; I am beginning to think he is right. Relaxing and laughing are also essential anti-stress factors (once you've done your exercise obviously). Happily I spent a lot of time researching both, so just relax and read on – you have all that to come.

So to cut down on environmental ageing always bear in mind the four Ss: sun, smoking, stress and sleep. None of the former three and lots of the latter.

'What about shagging?' says Rupert. 'That begins with an S.' He was joking, but sex actually is very anti-ageing. During sex the body secretes the steroid prohormone DHEA, which is linked to longevity. Sex is also relaxing and good for the circulatory system. In addition it reduces cholesterol and stimulates the oxygen supply to cells, as well as burning calories. And according to the Help the Aged website, sexually active people live longer.

So have lots of sex; it may even help you sleep better, and should certainly keep you out of the sun and away from smoking. If you can cut out anything that ages you from your life entirely, like the perfect American, then do. But nobody likes a swot. Even if it does begin with an S.

CHAPTER SIX

The Ageless Town

The smell of BO rises, just like heat. I didn't know this fact until I get on a sleeper train from Nice to Verona. As I look at my ticket and see the word *'couchette'* I think briefly how awful it would be to end up in a bed on top of one of those people with such ferocious BO that you just can't breathe, but I push the thought to one side.

Trains are my favourite form of transport; they are so romantic. There is a nice porter carrying my heavy bags and there is something extremely dreamy about speeding through the countryside at night on a train filled with expectant travellers (ideally those who have discovered the benefits of deodorant) bound for cities like Verona, Venice and Rome.

'You're further up, madame,' the porter tells me as we walk along the platform.

I should hope so, I think. This all looks a bit basic. But sadly, despite having asked for first class, I am in second. It may seem a bit spoiled to go first class, but in France, when you have as many children as I do, it costs you no more, so I have got used to it. Now it looks like I am going to have to get unused to it.

I smell the BO as soon as I get into the carriage. Please don't let him or her be in my compartment, I pray silently. But he is. And along with him is a Croatian member of the French Foreign Legion and a woman with dodgy hennaed hair, who eats salad constantly. How she can eat in this smell I have no idea.

I am on my way to Limone, a small village on the western side of Lake Garda in northern Italy. The people there have a genetic abnormality that causes them to live longer. The gene, called the Apo (short for Apolipoprotein) A1-MILANO induces healthy levels of good cholesterol (HDL), which results in a lower risk of vascular and heart diseases. A protein produced by this gene makes carriers virtually immune to cholesterol-related heart problems and strokes. This is intriguing. Apparently over 10 per cent of the 1,000-strong population is between one hundred and one hundred and ten years old. I imagine a town filled with grey-haired people pushing Zimmer frames up cobbled streets. I tell my friend Carla about it and she immediately suggests we go out there to investigate.

'They say if you're Italian you are more likely than others are to have the gene,' I tell her. 'So being half-Italian I think I'm in with a chance.'

'Do you think having an Italian name qualifies you?' she asks. Carla was named after a prostitute in *The Sky is Red*, a book by the Italian writer Giuseppe Berto.

'No.'

But I agree we should go together.

'How warm will it be?' I ask her. 'I was thinking of maybe just bringing shorts and T-shirts.'

'Are you sure about shorts?' asks Carla. 'I worry that you might find yourself upstaged by a certain young-at-heart journalist, i.e. *moi*, who is, even as we speak, practising her most winning smile and trying on various peek-a-boo outfits.'

Genetics are a fundamental factor in ageing. They determine to a certain extent how badly you're going to age. Everyone has met one of those really annoying types who never seems to get any older. 'It's in the genes,' they tell you when you ask what their secret is. In other words, you don't stand a chance.

Not only do genes determine how good you look,

they, rather more seriously, can also determine what diseases you're going to get.

A few weeks before I start my trip, Heather Bird, who runs a London health and beauty clinic called HB Health, suggests they do a genetic profile on me to determine what diseases I am susceptible to. I do a swab test and two weeks later am back at her clinic for the results. It is a Dr Klentze who will tell me what I am likely to die from. I am a little nervous as I arrive for our appointment. There is something to be said for not knowing these things. But Heather's argument, of course, is that if you know, you can act.

Before I see Dr Klentze I drink a shot of wheatgrass to steady my nerves. This is the most magical of drinks, several kilos of vegetables and all their goodness packed into a tiny shot. Someone once told me it's like eating three kilos of spinach, and it feels like it. Wheatgrass is one of those things that feels like it's really doing something when you drink it. So fully fortified I walk into his office. He is German. I know this not from his accent (which is soft) but from his glasses. Why is it that Germans tend to choose strange-coloured glasses? Something in the genes?

'How you age is determined by two factors,' he tells me once he's asked me to sit down, 'the environment and your genetics.'

Is he now going to tell me it's all over?

'But the good news is that genes are also under the control of the environment so what you eat, how you live, how much you exercise and so on is so important,' he continues. 'If you start to understand your genetic profile, not just as a condemnation, but rather a valuation, then you can use it in a positive way.'

I can't wait any longer.

'What's wrong with me?' I blurt out.

He ignores my question. Instead he tells me that although you might be predisposed to a certain disease in the future, there are certain things you can do to prevent it developing. For example, if you carry the gene that may lead to lung cancer, you can try to ward it off by taking a class of nutrients known as isothiocyanates, which are found in vegetables such as broccoli, cauliflower, watercress and cabbage. In other words, you can regulate the extent to which the gene is switched on or off (i.e. expressed) by the way you live.

'Am I going to have a heart attack?'

'No.' He smiles. 'At least not now.'

'And in the future?'

'Not as far as these tests show. But where you are at risk is with breast cancer. You have five times more chance of getting breast cancer than the average person. But it is manageable.'

I have often wondered how people take bad news from doctors. Of course, this is not really bad news, but I wouldn't call it good. Somehow it just washes over me for the moment, as if we're talking about someone else.

'How do I manage it?' I ask.

'If you take contraception you should come off the pill as it increases the risk of breast cancer. You should take vitamin B6 and vitamin D in the winter when you don't get much sun, take Procaine and 500 grams of calcium in the morning, as well as folic acid and GH3 along with Aslan. You should also increase your male hormone levels, but without the risk of increased oestrogen, so the only option is testosterone. Male hormones protect the breast against cancer. And you need to eat a lot of broccoli and cauliflower or take an indole carbinol supplement.'

My head is spinning. Wouldn't it just be easier to die?

'Don't worry, it's all written down in the report,' he assures me. 'I will write out a prescription for some gel with testosterone in it.'

'I don't want to have any more mammograms,' I tell him. 'My breasts have never been the same since.'

He tells me to prepare six weeks before a mammogram by taking a combination of vitamin D and calcium. Apparently this lowers the breast density and the mammogram doesn't damage them as much.

'But actually I would suggest an ultrasound instead,' he adds.

'Is there anything else I should be worried about?'

'Possibly osteoporosis but there's not a huge risk, just keep an eye on it. Thankfully you have no thrombosis and no Alzheimer's risk. In fact you have the opposite, a long life expectation due to low cholesterol.'

'If I did have the Alzheimer's gene, what could I do about it?'

'There's one really hard result that I have to tell people and that is the Alzheimer's result,' he replies. 'The only thing you can do is control the cholesterol. And you'd need to start as soon as possible; it takes a long time to develop, twenty to thirty years from the beginning to full-blown Alzheimer's. And of course mental and physical exercise is very important.'

Like Dr Wälli, Dr Klentze tells me that the most important single tool in anti-ageing is the immune system.

'It is your immune system that dictates whether or not you get cancer or other illnesses,' Klentze says, and goes on to say that you can store healthy white blood cells from your blood and reintroduce them if you become ill.

'Where do you store them?'

'At a laboratory, in temperatures of around minus 96 degrees. It costs around £60 a month.'

'I'm not sure most people can afford that. Is there anything else one can do?'

'You can strengthen the immune system with vitamin C, selenium and zinc. And there is a direct connection between psychology and immune system. Your mental strength is essential to any healing process; you can only heal yourself if you are free in your mind and have no doubts about your own ability. If you see people sneezing, for example, say, "I don't want to be ill," and concentrate. The power of the mind is incredible.' He smiles and leans back in his chair. 'Everybody has to make his goal age, an age you want to reach. My goal age is eighty-seven. Always remember that the medicine is secondary, number one is nutrition, lifestyle, exercise and mental attitude.'

I ask him about Limone and if I by any chance have the magic gene.

He lifts his red glasses and looks through his papers.

'No, you don't. But you're going to live a long time anyway.'

❊　　❊　　❊

Back on the train I am wondering if I will live through the night. Not only is the world's smelliest person getting smellier, but the member of the French Foreign Legion has plugged himself to an iPod and all I can hear is the tinny rhythm of loud house music.

I have tried my best to flirt with the guard and secure a compartment alone. It is a depressing truth that ten years ago it would have worked; now I need fifty euros cash, which I don't have. I phone Carla to complain. Carla is in her fifties, so more ahead in this ageing game than I am. 'Get used to it,' she says. 'When you get older, you become invisible. When I first lost the capacity to charm my way out of a situation it was a hell of a shock.' In my experience so far, the older I have become, the less I am noticed. And if you really honestly think about it, do you look at old people the same way as young people? Do you find them as interesting?

So here I am, stuck in travelling hell and no one cares. But all is not lost. According to a friend of Carla and mine, Rita Carter, who is a brain specialist and has written terribly intelligent books about how the brain works, the best way to avoid senile dementia, Alzheimer's and generally becoming a grumpy old woman is to listen to music you hate. So the Croatian is actually doing me a favour with his iPod.

'Just like any other organ in the body the brain is subject to ageing,' says Rita over dinner at Carla's house one evening, 'but what is perhaps more interesting is the change in attitude that happens. You start to think like an old person, adopt old attitudes. There is a refusal to accept new trends, to listen to new music, to adopt new fashions.'

'So the key to staying young is to listen to new music?' I ask, slightly incredulously.

Rita explains that listening to new music is creating new neural pathways in your brain. She tells me to think of my brain like a jelly. When you're young, it's very plastic and very wet, so very easy to change a route. A new piece of music, for example, makes a new pattern quickly, but when you're older that process of learning becomes more difficult to do.

'But why music?'

'Because all music is based on repetition. It is a slight change of basic melody, with enough change to keep you interested. Just the right combination of security and novelty that the brain is constantly seeking.'

'Can I not just listen to Mozart?' I ask. 'Do I have to listen to new music? I really hate new music.'

'I don't like any music,' says Carla.

'Yes, Carla has a bit of her brain missing, but let's not dwell on that,' says Rita.

She goes on to explain that in order to avoid degenerative brain diseases you need to keep creating connections in the brain. It is all about keeping the neural pathways open and creating new patterns by experiencing new things.

'In Southend, where I used to live, the tide would go out a long way and leave acres of mud flats with tiny rivulets in them,' she tells us. 'The brain is just like that – always follows the same pattern if it can. The challenge as you get older is to keep producing new patterns.'

'What do you personally do to keep your neural pathways active?' I ask her.

'Well, one of the things I do is read the computer press and keep up with technology,' she says. 'It is all moving so incredibly fast, one day little social gatherings like this one we're having will be seen as eccentric and everyone will socialise in cyberspace.'

'Like Second Life,' says Carla.

'What's Second Life?' I ask.

'God, has she aged or what?' Carla says, looking at me pityingly. 'It's this online thing where you live a life in cyberspace, you have houses, love affairs, children. It's a proper life in cyberspace.'

'How can you have affairs in cyberspace?' I ask. 'How do you have sex?'

'You have cybersex,' says Rita.

'Is it as good as real sex?' I ask.

'Much better,' says Carla, 'and less messy.'

According to Rita you can exercise the brain in just the same way you exercise any other muscle. Just before you go to bed at night, for example, spend an hour going over the day's events two or three times in your head. That encodes them more firmly in your brain. Then sleep on it and repeat the exercise in the morning.

Sadly Alzheimer's is genetic, so if you've got the gene you're going to get it. Having said that, Rita tells the story of an Oxford don who went to his doctor to complain that when he played chess he could only think eight moves in advance. 'I used to be able to think twelve moves ahead,' he told his doctor. Within four months he was dead from Alzheimer's. The disease had already eaten away 60 per cent of his brain but because he had so many connections he was still functioning better than the rest of us. 'You can't stop it coming,' says Rita, 'but it destroys connections, so if you've got a million connections then it's not going to affect you as much as if you have 100,000 connections. You may even be dead before you notice that you have it.'

Rita says that in order to increase your connections, apart from listening to strange music, you can do crosswords, mental arithmetic, chess, scrabble and word games. You should start as early as you can and do it all your life. Also, having another language delays the onset of Alzheimer's for four years on average.

'Every act of learning leaves a trace in the brain,' she says. 'The more of those you have, the denser the material is, the more connections you have, the more of them you can cut and still have a workable brain.'

In the end, if you do have Alzheimer's it will eventually kill you. It is a progressive closing down of brain functions that starts in areas to do with memory but once it gets down to areas that control breathing, for example, you simply forget to breathe.

Of course Alzheimer's is not the only thing we have to worry about. Rita believes that an enormous amount of apparent senility is caused by the wrong drugs being prescribed to old people.

'You might as well just mix up all the drugs in the world and put them in a huge vat and invite people to come and stuff them down their throats,' she says. 'I saw it with my mother; the incompetence was breathtaking.'

Rita tells us how her mother was admitted to hospital after a minor heart attack. The neighbour who took her in gave all the drugs Rita's mother was on to the nurse at casualty. One of them was Prozac. One of the medications the doctors prescribed when she was admitted was a beta-blocker.

'Prozac takes ages to get out of the system,' says Rita, 'and it reacts very badly with beta-blockers so as soon as my mother comes round she starts hallucinating that there are people living in the curtain around her bed.'

Word soon goes round that she is just a senile old lady and no one takes any notice of her. When she asks to go to the loo they ignore her. Finally she gets so desperate she gets out of bed herself and falls flat on her face.

'She comes out of hospital completely black and blue from head to foot,' says Rita.

We move on to discuss the lack of respect society has for the elderly. Rita's theory is that mobile and progressive societies where life is changing and the young want to move have little time or need for the elderly.

'In peasant societies the elders still hold knowledge that is useful to the next generation,' she says. 'What could my mother give to me? She had nothing to say about the world I was living in; she was living by rules from the 1950s. There aren't many eternal verities that one generation can pass to the other. How do you truly emotionally retain respect for a person whose life was forged in such different circumstances and has nothing to do with yours?'

'And nowadays they're not even in the same place,' adds Carla. 'Plus people are living such horrendous amounts of years now when they should have died in their seventies. You're in the dustbin of life.'

I have never before been so relieved to get up at five o'clock in the morning as I am when we arrive in Verona. My next connection is a train to Desenzano del Garda. I seem to have arrived in a twilight zone. I am rarely travelling at this time and there are not many people about, but those who are around are immigrants, obviously going to and from jobs Italians don't want to do. At Desenzano there is a bus to Limone but I have just missed it and it is two hours before the next one so I get a taxi. My driver is about seventy and listens with finger-clicking enthusiasm to Italian pop songs all the way there, some eighty kilometres. Maybe he has the Apo A1 gene. I ask him if he's from Limone.

'No, I'm from Desenzano,' he tells me.

'Do they live longer in Limone than Desenzano?'

'Oh, yes,' he tells me, finally switching off the radio. There is only one thing worse than Italian pop songs and that's French pop songs. 'It's the air up there, and the cheese from the hill-top. They eat well there.'

We arrive in Limone at around a quarter to seven.

There is no one about, so no centenarians to check out. I sit on the terrace of the hotel and look out over the lake. There are mountains behind me and mountains mirrored in the water. The nature is lovely, but the village has been ruined by too much development. Limone and the surrounding region used to be a lemon-growing area.

Goethe went past Limone in a boat on 13 September 1786 (possibly the first of many Germans to do so) and was captivated by its beauty: 'This morning was magnificent, a bit cloudy, but calm as the sun rose. We sailed past Limone, with its terraced gardens perched on the hill slopes. It was a spectacle of abundance and grace. The entire garden is composed of rows of square white pillars at regular intervals, topped by heavy beams to cover the trees that grow during winter. The slow crossing made it possible to better observe and contemplate this pleasing spectacle.'

You can still see the stone pillars where the farmers would put mirrors to reflect the sun and give more heat to the lemons. Until the 1940s the town was only accessible via the mountains or the lake. It must have been heavenly. Then mass tourism arrived and instead of being a landscape covered in golden lemon orchards it is covered with cheap and nasty hotels. As my taxi driver said, 'Progress has taken us backwards.'

Carla arrives later that day. She and I have a very different philosophy to ageing. The first thing she does when she gets to Limone is buy a packet of cigarettes. I tell her for about the thousandth time how appallingly bad smoking is.

'I know all that,' she says, puffing away and really annoying the Germans who are sitting behind us. 'But I don't want to live to be very old. I have longevity in the whole of my family so I need to do something to die younger.'

Part of the reason Carla is so reluctant to age is that her mother has taken to old age extremely badly. She is in denial, she no longer feels part of our world and seems to have given up on life. Carla has bought her a DVD player so she can watch films but she refuses to learn how to use it.

'The world has so moved on since you were in it, I tell her,' says Carla.

Carla's mother won't talk to any of her old friends and then complains that they never call. This once intelligent and politically aware woman will now sit during a discussion with her head hanging down, unwilling to participate in any conversation, even though she is perfectly able to. She refuses to take any exercise whatsoever. She had a hip replacement that has not worked well because she didn't do the physio-therapy.

According to Carla she only opens her mouth to criticise. 'She even complained when I said I was coming to Italy,' she says. 'She used to love Italy.'

That evening Carla and I walk down to the water and find a restaurant for dinner. So far I have not spotted one old person with the special gene. The only thing the people of Limone seem to have in common is a control-freak gene. At the otherwise charming Hotel Alla Noce they refused to let me eat breakfast outside. When Carla parked her car she was told to move it about half a centimetre to the right. Then when we were having a drink I put my (naked) feet on the side of a rather ugly plastic chair and was told by the waiter that 'we're in a restaurant'. Carla suggests the name Limone (lemon) might come from the perpetual look of disapproval on the faces of the staff there. The good news is, I suppose, that if it's a control-freak gene that is making them live longer I'm going to live to one hundred and fifty.

But the waiters at dinner are nice. As always we are surrounded by Germans. I had not imagined that Limone would be the number-one German travel destination but it seems so. We drink a lovely bottle of Italian red wine and eat well.

'If I were with Rita now we'd order another bottle of wine and smoke another five cigarettes,' grumbles Carla as we leave to go back to the hotel. 'I'll probably live a month longer now.'

I wake at half-past six in the morning. The sun is rising over the mountains and there is a thin mist on the lake. I sit down on one of the benches on the terrace at the hotel. I remember a joke that Norrie, a friend of mine, once told me.

An old man is sitting on a park bench crying. A woman who is walking by stops to ask him what's wrong.

'I'm ninety-four years old,' he says. 'I have a twenty-eight-year-old wife. She's not only stunningly beautiful but every morning she brings me breakfast in bed, then she bathes me and covers me in rose oil. Every night we make love after a fabulous home-cooked dinner. She treats me like a god.'

'So why are you crying?' asks the woman.

'I can't remember where I live,' he says.

In their quest to look good, women (and men) often ignore the other major factor in ageing well or badly: the mind and the attitude. There is no point in having luscious lips if you can't remember where you've put your lip gloss or what the names of your grandchildren are when they run into your arms to be kissed by those luscious lips. Just as there is no point in looking good on the outside if you're just bitter and angry on the inside. If you have an attitude like Carla's mother then no amount of Botox is going to make you seem younger.

As Rita says, 'Not being open to new ideas is very ageing.'

Norrie, whom I mentioned above, is a relatively new friend of mine. He is seventy-five but could easily pass for sixty or less. His attitude is great. I went to stay with him along with my children one summer and what really struck me was his openness to everything. If the children came up with some ridiculous plan he wouldn't say, 'Don't be so stupid, of course you can't'; he'd talk to them about it, even consider it, and then more often than not go along with it. He really loved having them around. He was as playful as they are and looked at the same things in wonder. 'Years wrinkle the skin,' he told me, 'but to give up enthusiasm wrinkles the soul. Youth is not a time of life, it is a state of mind.'

He moved from England, where he taught at a university, to France with his wife, Mary, sixteen years ago. 'We did it partly to stay young,' he says. 'New language, new culture, new home.' They have a donkey, three dogs, geese, ducks, rabbits and a huge vegetable garden. Every morning Norrie walks up a practically vertical hill to the local farm to collect his fresh milk. They make almost everything they eat, including butter and yoghurt. 'We're never going to get old,' he tells me, 'because there isn't time to get old.'

Retiring for many people is the beginning of death. Work can be a lifeline. Look at what happened to Margot Fonteyn, aged forty-two, when Rudolf Nureyev came along to partner her. Suddenly, instead of retiring, she was bouncing around like a twenty-year-old. And who can blame her with Rudi as a partner?

One of the most elegant old people I know is my father. He is eighty-four and still wears linen suits and panama hats. His mind is as sharp as it always was. He is a writer and an opera critic. He hates being old, but, when he joins us for dinner in Limone one evening, I ask him if there are any advantages to old age.

'You get to go half-price on the train, and mosquitoes don't bite me,' he says as we sit on the terrace of the hotel overlooking Lake Garda.

He adds that in Rome pretty girls get up to give him their seats on buses. 'My response to them is always this: "Signorina, you are too kind. But you must understand that it is only a rare and incurable disease that has reduced me to this state. I am in fact only twenty-three years old and if you'll permit it, I will take you home tonight and make love to you all night to prove it.'"

He is a bit shocked to learn that Carla is over fifty. 'Never introduce me to anyone over eighteen,' he says to me when she's not listening. 'Apart from Mary, I like Mary.' Mary is over eighteen but very pretty. The first time they met he declared himself madly in love with her.

He says other advantages include not having to pay to get into museums and the fact that your social life is extremely limited as most people you know have died. My father doesn't like socialising. He tells me he called an old school friend the other day. 'Aren't you dead yet?' she asked when he told her who he was.

Rather like Rita, he believes the brain is the single most important thing in ageing.

'In terms of my physical appearance a lot has changed,' he says. 'But really for me it's not a problem because I have retained my intellectual level. You know the brain decides everything. If you don't have hope or interests, even your body will lose hope and interest. If you have hope and interest your body will give you the necessary energy. It all depends on your psychological attitude.'

My father tells Carla and me the story of the Austrian writer Stefan Zweig who was in the process of writing some operas with Richard Strauss when the Nazis came along. Strauss said they should just carry on working as if the Nazis weren't there. In a few years they would be gone, he reasoned, but the opera would live on. Zweig didn't have the courage to think about life after the Nazis and killed himself.

'If you believe in your own immortality and your capacity to survive you can live freely,' he says. 'Until you're dead, you are immortal. If you start to say, "I could live two, three years," it's the beginning of the end. You have to have long-term projects. And always remember that old age is a bad thing, but it is the only thing that stops you from dying.'

He compares old age to Dante's *Inferno*. 'Abandon all hope, ye who enter here' is written above the gates of hell. For most people it is a state without hope. The way to handle old age intelligently is to approach it with hope and even some illusions.

'Old people can't be young but they can succeed in giving themselves the illusion of being young,' he says. 'For example, men and women who dye their hair at home. Everyone knows they do it but they think that others think they have black hair and that they look younger. This is a mad idea but it helps people to feel better. Of course, it also helps the manufacturers of hair dye to make lots of money.'

In the Limone museum there is lots of information about the famous gene. It was first discovered around thirty years ago when Limone resident Valerio Dagnoli went for a check-up and his doctor told him his cholesterol was way over average. 'But I feel fine,' said Valerio. No amount of pills or treatments would bring the level down and eventually they took him to Milan where a Professor Cesare Sirtori ran tests for four years until the abnormality was diagnosed.

There is a huge family tree showing the origins of it as well as today's carriers. It dates back to 1644 when Rosa Giovanelli married Cristofero Pomeroli. Rosa lived to be eighty-four, which is a pretty respectable age to get to now, let alone then, when most people died before they were ten. Other descendants include Caterina Tita Pomeroli, who died on 14 April 1845 aged eighty-one, and Maria Catarina Pomeroli who died in 1883, aged eighty-two. Her son Benedetto did even better, dying aged ninety-one. One name stands out on the vast family tree that takes up a whole wall of the museum – that of Tracy Diane Flatman, who married a carrier of the gene called Davide Girarde in 1991. Sadly their son Louis, born in 2001, has not got it.

There have been several conferences held at Limone to research and investigate the gene, such as the grippingly entitled Fourth Apolipoproteins Congress held in October 1995. In 2003 a group of scientists headed by Professor Steven Nissen from the Cleveland Clinic Foundation succeeded in reproducing the protein to make a drug from it. It is being developed at the moment. So maybe sometime soon we'll all have access to a substitute of the Limone gene.

Carla and I go down to the lake for a swim. I have yet to see an old person, but maybe they're all behind young façades. We find some sun-loungers and settle in for the morning. After about five minutes I need to cool off. I get into the water and find myself walking like an old person. Taking care with each step, worried about falling, trying to avoid sharp stones. It is windy and the water is rough. Finally, despite my attention, I fall in sideways. This must be one of the worst things about getting old: not being able to do things that you just used to take for granted. As my father says, 'Ageing means a loss of control over your own body. Whereas ten years ago you commanded and your body responded 100 per cent, now it responds with 60 to

70 per cent and not more. It begins to become a conflict.'

Yeats put it very well. 'An aged man is but a paltry thing, a tattered coat upon a stick.' And a middle-aged woman trying to walk into a lake is not much better.

As I struggle out of the water I see an aged gentleman swimming close by but when I ask him in Italian if he's from Limone he answers in German. Then I spot an elderly couple at the water's edge, fully dressed, splashing water from the lake on their arms, legs and faces in an effort to cool down. The man wets the back of his wife's neck with the water.

'Do you come from Limone?' I ask.

They tell me that they do. I ask them about the special gene.

'We don't have it, not everyone does, but a lot of our friends do and it is unique to Limone,' says the woman. 'They don't even have it in the next village.'

'Last week there were two funerals here,' says the man. 'One was for someone one hundred and three, and the other one hundred and seven, but to us that's fairly normal.'

I get back to the sun-lounger feeling exhausted after my morning's tough reporting.

'I could do with a green tea,' I tell Carla.

'I could do with a huge coffee and a cigarette followed by a carafe of wine and a lobster,' she replies cheerfully.

Maybe Carla's pro-ageing system is one I should try. At least I'd be too drunk to go swimming, or if I did I would expect to have trouble getting out of the lake.

On our way to the hotel we pass the Limone museum. The young girl whose job seems to be constantly to clean it comes running out when she sees us.

'If you want to know about the gene, he knows all about it,' she says, pointing conspiratorially at a man, in a leather goods shop opposite, wearing a checked shirt. 'He's got it.'

Amelio Segala is fifty-three years old but looks much younger. He is tall and well built, with a full head of thick, black hair. He has lived in Limone all his life and was one of a group of gene-carrying locals who were taken to America where they spent twenty-eight days being tested. His parents have the gene, as do all his siblings. His father died aged ninety-one and his mother is seventy-eight and still going strong. I ask him what having the gene means to him.

'That's too big a question,' he says. In his leather shop he has an article written in an American magazine from 1993. It is kept under some leather goods in the envelope it was sent in. There is a picture of him and

Davide Girarde, the gene carrier who married the Englishwoman. He also has letters from Americans who read the article. They are addressed to Amelio Segala, Limone, Italy and asking where they can buy the gene.

'I wrote back and explained it isn't the sort of thing you can buy,' he tells me. 'I think it came from way back in the seventeenth century when they just ate fresh lemons, olive oil, fresh fish and other good things. But actually I think the key to staying young is *amore*.'

He winks at us and laughs. We make our escape and back at the hotel we sit down to order a drink. Carla orders a large beer while I go for a still mineral water.

'Ah, that's better,' Carla says, taking a sip. 'A life of success is the one for Helena, a life of excess is the one for me!'

CHAPTER SEVEN

To Jamaica with Love (Stress-Free)

This threatens to be the most arduous of my research trips. I am going to Jamaica to see if chilling out can be as effective as massage, Botox or face creams when it comes to slowing the ageing process. Jamaica is renowned as one of the most stress-free places on earth. The people are so laid back they're mainly prostrate, the climate makes you want to do nothing, and the rum cocktails don't help.

It is Rupert's idea. He is worried about where this book is taking me and has decided to try to introduce me to some natural anti-aging methods before I go totally off the rails. Although I am making good progress when it comes to my genes, face creams and water intake, I have been threatening to resort to more radical methods in my battle against *the* wrinkle. It is not budging and I hate it. Rupert suggests I try a stress-free few days to see if that helps, before visiting a dermatologist.

'You may find just a few days relaxing is what you really need, rather than a needle filled with poison,' he says. 'You're always so stressed and unless you deal with that I'm not sure any amount of creams is going to help.'

Rupert has a point. While researching ageing, I have come to realise that next to sun exposure, my own greatest environmental ageing enemy is stress. I am not a normal person when it comes to stress; I am more frenzied than normal people. Friends and relations are always telling me to 'stay Zen' or 'relax', and it makes me want to punch them. In fact, it stresses me out even more.

I hate the way people think they have a say in how stressed you are or should be. Why is it any of their business? If I want to run around like a headless chicken, then that's up to me. How dare they deprive me of it? But irrespective of that the undeniable fact is: stress kills. And it ages you. My friend Iona has no children, no money worries and has been living in India for the last six years surrounded by gorgeous young men who adore her. Does she have a single, tiny, minuscule wrinkle? No. And she's never had Botox.

My Italian aunt is another example of someone with what I would define as a largely stress-free life. She gets up every day around 10 a.m., spends an hour in the bathroom while my uncle prepares her breakfast, then they go shopping for lunch. She might visit the hairdresser or beautician if she's feeling really energetic. After lunch they have a sleep, then my uncle goes out to buy the food for dinner, or they eat out. If they stay in, he always washes up. As a result of this existence she is almost eighty (a fact I would not be able to reveal had she not already disinherited me due to my memoir about my Italian family) and looks sixty. So if you don't want to age, stop reading this now and do nothing for the rest of your life.

Stress is so difficult to control because it is so difficult to define. And quite often we're stressed and don't even realise it. When I went to HB Health in London a few weeks ago, they hooked me up to a machine meant to make you Zen. I sat in a chair, breathing deeply with monitors all over me. I thought I was completely relaxed, my eyes were shut and I felt great, but the screen was going haywire.

'You're at the highest stress level,' I was told by Carmen, who was monitoring me. 'Try to relax just a little.' I tried my best, but I couldn't significantly calm the Zen-machine down.

Everyone agrees that combating stress will help you

to slow down the ageing process and so reduce visible signs of ageing. Dr Jeya Prakash, a Harley Street-based clinical doctor, tells me that chakra meditation is one of the best things you can do to slow down the ageing process as it balances your hormones and regenerates cells.

The hypnotherapist Barbara Ford-Hammond says that totally relaxing can actually add years to your life. 'You age from the inside out so you need to be able to totally relax your organs for them to work in perfect harmony,' she says. 'If you can totally relax for ten to fifteen minutes a day you are giving your body the equivalent of three hours' sleep. People say they don't have the time but it is just a question of priorities.'

So off I go to Jamaica with my husband for a whole week of sun and stress-free existence to see if I come back home looking any younger.

The flight starts off well.

'You're being upgraded to upper class,' says the man checking us in. I have never flown upper class or first class in my life. I expect great things. Suddenly the prospect of a nine-and-a-half-hour flight is wonderful. Nine and a half hours to be pampered and drink champagne. We are well looked after, fed, and spoiled, our chairs turned into beds and they even give us little lip glosses. We seem to have our own stewardess called Sam at our constant beck and call. Two rows up there is a Colin Firth lookalike. My stress levels are already way down and we haven't even got to Jamaica. However, much as I enjoy this, I am now already dreading the way home when we are booked to fly economy. See what I mean about my stress levels?

We land at around 2 p.m. at Montego Bay Airport. It is hot but cloudy. Immigration is lengthy and irritating. There are loads of people, partly because tomorrow is the semi-final of the Cricket World Cup. I see an American bump into a local with a vast bag he is lugging around.

'I'm so sorry,' says the American.

'No problem,' says the Jamaican. 'In Jamaica nothing is a problem.'

Much better. This is the kind of attitude I am here to adopt.

I manoeuvre myself next to the Colin Firth lookalike in the queue and end up securing his phone number for my friend Iona, as he travels to India a lot.

'Shameless,' my husband calls me. 'Selfless' is what I call it, though quite why I should help Iona to stay even younger-looking than me I don't know.

Once out of immigration we meet Kevin, who is

driving us to our first destination: Jake's on Treasure Beach, favourite chill-out spot of Kate Moss and her pals.

The funny thing about the Caribbean, I notice as we drive to Jake's, is that there are lots of people sitting, standing, lying about doing absolutely nothing. I see one man sitting on the porch of his half-finished house, drinking a beer.

'Get up and finish your house before you start drinking,' I want to yell at him.

I don't know if it's my northern work ethic or what, but seeing people lounge about makes me nervous. Maybe this Jamaica trip wasn't such a good idea. Everything seems a bit chaotic. There are goats and cows wandering around, shacks tumbling down and rotting cars lining the road. The most organised thing about Jamaica is without doubt the school children, who all wear impeccable uniforms, the boys in beautifully ironed khaki shirts and trousers and the girls in white starched shirts with navy-blue pinafore dresses. Their hair is braided into neat plaits. We are driving through the countryside at the end of the school day and they all look as if they have just got dressed: how do they do it?

❖   ❖   ❖

Jake's was designed and built by the owner's mother, Sally, who has 'a big heart and a bohemian spirit', according to the brochure. It shows. Our room is sweet, and the location stupendous, right on the seafront, but it's all a bit basic for me. As a child I hated camping and this comes close to it. I like order, routine, cleanliness, comfort. I never went through a Bohemian phase as a teenager and every time I tried to smoke a joint I had panic attacks about losing control. Needless to say, my favourite place to holiday is Switzerland; I'd say I'm about as Bohemian as Margaret Thatcher.

Still, even I can't fail to see that Jake's has a certain charm. The cottages, dotted about a stretch of coastline, are all well built, colourful and idiosyncratic. Some of them are Moroccan in style. There are colours everywhere – blue, lavender, pink, ochre, green. The walls are made out of a mixture of stones, shells and tiles; everything seems to blend in well with nature.

The main reception area is a bay shape overlooking the sea with a pink cottage and kitchen. There are around eight tables with faded but colourful tablecloths where the clientele meet for breakfast, dinner and lunch, along with most of the neighbourhood's stray dogs. These dogs are not daft. Jake's attracts the kind of soppy person (like me) who will feed them as opposed to kicking them.

Carla is even worse than I am. She would probably never leave Jake's for fear of the dogs starving. Whenever she comes to France she launches a one-woman crusade to free all the hunting dogs in our village that are tied up and left to bark for most of the day. Her theory is that dogs are much nicer than people.

They are certainly more intelligent than most of the clientele at Jake's. There are at least three women here, alone and wearing floppy hats and strange sandals, talking to the dogs, naming them silly names and endlessly petting them. I even heard one argument between two of them as to which of the names they had individually given the mangy stray best suited him.

There is a salt-water swimming pool between the dining area and the sea. Sally is mad about the Catalan architect Antonio Gaudí (I suppose someone has to be) and it is the pool that shows this most. It is shaped like a kidney but decorated more like a carnival float. It is exploding with colours – think of every colour you've ever seen and then add some more. Along the sides of the pool there are shapes made out of mosaics that look like abstract lizards, fish and snakes.

Close to the pool is the bar, which is run by Duggie, a local who has been around for ever and is, according to the hotel blurb, a legend. To me, he encompasses the two things I find least attractive about the Caribbean: he is stoned and surly; never a great combination.

'What fresh juices do you have, please?' I ask him after our fourteen-hour journey.

'Everything I have is fresh,' he responds grumpily.

'Great. I'll have a fresh pineapple juice.'

'It's from a can,' responds the 'legend'.

As well as the sea practically coming into our room (my first thought was obviously what happened if we had a tsunami), we have the best shower I have ever seen. It is outside. After dinner we shower under the stars with water heated from solar panels.

I sleep well until 3 a.m. and then I do my classic waking-up-and-worrying trick. This is not something new but definitely something I had hoped to avoid in Jamaica. I am meant to be destressing. But no, I stress about being too tired tomorrow to properly destress. I'm thinking about the fact that I have no mobile phone signal or access to the internet. Has my riveting piece about first love gone into the *Daily Mail* today? Will Eli remember that tonight it is the girls' art class? How am I going to write another 60,000 words of this book by my deadline? Why is the adapter plug they gave me for my mobile phone (with no signal) not working? If I sneeze will I wake Rupert? What will I wear to the wedding of the Colin Firth lookalike and my friend Iona?

Something about this relaxing and destressing is not really working. Yet.

After a couple of days at Jake's we pack up and get into a car to drive across the island. We are headed to Ian Fleming's old house on Jamaica's northern coast, a place called Goldeneye. It is where he spent two months a year and wrote all the Bond books. The journey is fine if you like bumper cars. Jamaicans don't seem to worry about what side of the road you're meant to drive on; they just go down the middle beeping loudly. There are signs at the side of the road saying: 'Don't be in a hurry to reach Eternity.' That goes double for me. It is the final of the Cricket World Cup so throughout the journey we listen to the Sri Lanka versus Australia game. My husband wishes he were there, but most of all he wishes the Australians don't win. I wish I were anywhere but in this car. Apart from Eternity, obviously. After four hours we arrive.

'Welcome to Goldeneye,' says a charming black woman dressed in white. 'Here is the house cocktail. It's just a little rum, fresh apple and lime. You'll be staying in the Ian Fleming Villa. There is a private beach, pool, several bedrooms, each with its own outside bath and shower, any laundry you have just put it in the basket and Housekeeping will collect it. The mini bar is over there, just help yourself. Should you have too many Goldeneyes and collapse there is an emergency medical button you can push for help. Your masseuse will be here at six. Nico, our personal trainer (Italian, very muscular) is on hand to take you jet-skiing, running, canoeing, whatever you like. Can I do anything else for you?'

OK, so now I'm relaxed.

I am writing this at the desk where Ian Fleming tapped out all the Bond novels on a gold-plated Royal typewriter. There was something impressively vulgar about the man's taste, but not his house: it's a master-piece of minimalism. The room I am in is as big as a barn; the window stretches almost across the whole wall. Outside I can hear the sea lapping on my private raked beach, a chicken who has decided to visit, crickets, tree frogs and various other Caribbean creatures.

Patrick Leigh Fermor describes the house brilliantly in his book *The Traveller's Tree*: 'Here, on the headland, Ian Fleming has built a house called Goldeneye that might serve as a model for new houses in the tropics. Trees surround it on all sides except the sea, which it almost overhangs. Great windows capture every breeze, to cool, even on the hottest day, the large white rooms. The windows that look towards the sea are glassless but equipped with outside shutters against rain: enormous quadrilaterals surrounded by dark wooden frames which enclose a prospect of sea and cloud and sky, and tame the elements, as it were, into an overhanging fresco of which one could never tire.'

The bathroom is outside, in a sort of secret, bamboo-walled garden, filled with exotic plants. In the evening oversized candles light your way to a free-standing Victorian bath amid palm trees on a wood-panelled stage. To the left is a large shower, and next to the bedroom door a rectangular marble slab with a brass sink on top of it. A large mirror hangs above it, its frame made up of tiny shells.

The ground is covered with pale, old stone. It is lovely to think that Ian Fleming must have padded about here barefoot as he prepared to take his pre-cocktail bath underneath the stars, plotting Bond's next move. The ground in the rest of the 'room' is a mixture of flagstones and tiny stones. Candles are dotted about as well as plants; some vibrant green, some bright red and pink. No other decoration is needed. Half of the area is protected by a wooden awning, but obviously if it is raining and you want a bath you'll be treated to a shower as well.

On the first evening, Orah arrives at six o'clock to give me a massage. It is a deeply relaxing treatment combining yoga, massage, rain-drop oil therapy and hot stones. She sets up in the sunken garden overlooking the sea. Orah is a nice-looking woman of around fifty. She is Jamaican but was born in New York and has lived there, Washington DC and Florida. 'But I finally made it back here,' she tells me.

I immediately feel I'm in the hands of a professional. Her movements are confident, practised, mostly soothing but painful on some of the areas my stress accumulates. She says my whole trapezius muscle is totally tight.

'I'm a bit stressed,' I admit.

'I feel it, honey,' she says, placing hot stones in strategic areas and easing out the stress and toxins from my body. It is an amazing sensation. I remember my conversation with Dr Wälli at the Clinique La Prairie in Switzerland, that we have so little human contact in our culture nowadays that there is an increasing need for treatments like massages.

Not necessarily a positive thought, but there is something really comforting about being touched and massaged, especially with lime-grass and lavender oil. I soon find that I drift off and then come back round; I am in a sort of haze of relaxation. This must be taking years off me. I fall asleep in the evening sun and wake up under the stars.

I ask Orah if she thinks stress is ageing.

'Oh, yes, most definitely,' she says. 'It attacks every organ. Oprah did a show about women who defy age, recently. There was one woman who was seventy but who looked fifty, another who was forty and looked twenty. They were amazing, and they had one thing in common.'

'What, they had hot-stone massages every day?'

'No, they were single,' she says.

So the key to looking young is staying unmarried? I remember an amazing statistic I read somewhere that married men live longer than unmarried men but that for women the opposite is true. Do relationships equal stress? At least for women? I admit that there are times when Rupert is away that I think life is less complicated without him. I just focus on the children and fit into their pattern, early dinner, a bit of jumping on the trampoline and early bed. It suits me fine. But I do start to miss him after a few days.

An older friend of mine says that she used to cherish her moments alone. 'It was the only time I felt I wasn't being pulled in all directions,' she told me once. But then being alone is terrible. I have a friend who is so fed up with life alone that she is going to try internet dating. 'I'll probably get murdered on the first date so that will solve everything,' she says.

Orah is a clay sculptor as well as a masseuse, and I can tell as her fingers delicately yet firmly work their way over my body.

She tells me about a book she is reading called *The Secret*. Its author maintains that one night she was trying to read something and she couldn't see the text so reached for her glasses. She couldn't find them. She told herself that she didn't need them. 'I have perfect vision,' she said. Three days later she did. Orah thinks you can apply this to anti-ageing.

'I have no wrinkles,' I say, thinking in particular about the most-hated one.

'No,' says Orah. 'It can't be negative. You should say instead, "I have the smooth, perfect skin of a twenty-year-old."'

'I have the smooth, perfect skin of a twenty-year-old,' I repeat. 'How do I look?'

'I think you have to keep going for a few days,' says Orah.

Rupert and I have dinner down on our private beach.

There are candles lighting our way to a table laid for two overlooking the sea. The sound of the waves competes with Bob Marley for dominance. I have noticed that wherever you go in Jamaica Bob Marley is playing. 'There's always a snake in paradise,' says Rupert. I'm glad no one hears him. I get the feeling not liking Bob Marley in Jamaica is not an option.

After dinner we try to work our home cinema to watch a Bond film but we can't even get the cupboard open so we go to bed instead.

I lie in our large double bed repeating my mantra. There is a huge bamboo frame around the bed from which muslin cloth hangs as protection against mosquitoes. I can hear the sea outside and the crickets settling in for the night. I am sleepy, relaxed and protected – and in the morning, maybe, I will have the smooth perfect skin of a twenty-year-old.

CHAPTER EIGHT

No Woman, No Cry

As I stand naked in my outdoor bathroom looking at myself in the mirror, a rather depressing thought occurs to me. I now look better with clothes than without. It used to be the other way round.

There was a time when I would happily have pranced down Oxford Street wearing nothing but a straw hat, but those days are gone. In fact, come to think of it, I did prance down the Brompton Road just in my underwear for a bet. It was in 1990 and my then flatmates, both male, bet me £60 to do it. Back then that was a week's rent, so I went for it. I'm not sure I'd do it for £6,000 now. Not that anyone would stump up a week's rent to see me in my underwear, even if it is matching, nowadays.

Of course, millions of women all over the world are

going through similar angst. Even the *Mona Lisa* is not immune. According to tests carried out at the Louvre Museum she is ageing more rapidly than she used to. Mind you, she is nearly five hundred years old. I've got a bit of a way to go yet.

I try to analyse what's happened to my body. Three children and a lot of years is what's happened to it. My tummy is not flat (having said that, it never was), my legs are OK, still thin, but the skin around the knees looks saggy and old. My breasts are still not too bad. They could be bigger, but the years have not done too much damage. The most dramatic thing to hit them was a mammogram, which seemed to flatten them.

I tried some breast creams to remedy the situation but didn't see much of a result. Of all of them, the Decléor Perfect Bust I mention in Chapter five was probably the best one. Even that, however, made no difference to my nipples, which look a bit sad after all that breast-feeding. I once complained about this to Carla, who very sweetly showed up at my house shortly afterwards with a pink parcel from Agent Provocateur. Inside was a lip gloss and something called a nipple balm that promised to titillate my nipples and give them back the spring in their step.

I immediately opened the lip gloss and put some on.

'How do I look?' I asked Carla.

'You look like, oh my God, your lips look like nipples; you've put the wrong one on,' she shrieked.

Very amusing.

Anyway, I did try the nipple balm later and, oh wonder, it did seem to make my nipples look pert and rosy, like they once used to. The effect lasted around half an hour and if I ever want to impress anyone with my pert nipples I'll be sure to wear it, although it's not exactly something I carry around in my handbag.

But back to my decaying body. With my second child, Bea, I had a caesarean. There is a nasty lump of flesh just over the scar that adds to the world-weary look. My buttocks are OK, they could be firmer, and there are some slight stretch marks on them from where I've gained or lost weight too quickly, I forget which. I notice that just at the junction with my legs there is a rather un-necessary piece of flesh. When did that suddenly get there? And everything seems to be pointing downwards.

Despite the fact that I am almost the same weight now as I was at university I seem to have no waist. That dreaded middle-aged spread is arriving. My whole midriff seems to be shapeless. And I haven't even had the fun of getting fatter. How unfair is that?

My arms are OK, no bat's-wings, those bits that

hang so attractively from the upper arms of women. Yet. I suppose it's only a matter of time. The skin around my elbows looks worn, but I already know there's nothing you can do about that. 'You need that skin to be able to move your arm,' Dr Orentreich, a dermatologist I saw in New York, told me. What if I agree not to move my arm, can it be removed?

Basically my body is no longer doing me any favours.

I look at my face in the mirror. The good news is that after two days at Goldeneye I do look more relaxed, browner (despite the fact that I obviously have NOT been sitting in the sun) and actually a bit younger. Maybe my husband was right. Or perhaps my mantra worked overnight? My body is still looking the same as ever but perhaps I should try a 'I have the beautiful body of a twenty-year-old' tonight.

Meanwhile we have an appointment with Nico this morning, the Italian fitness guru. We are going to do a Pilates class. For years I have listened to people droning on about how marvellous Pilates is and felt that it is something I should try, but until now I never have. I am amazed when my husband agrees to join me. He's about as far away from the 'green tea and Pilates' culture as you can get. His idea of a good breakfast involves bacon, sausages and eggs, and any exercise normally includes a bike, a golf club or at the very least a tennis racket. But at the appointed hour he is dressed in his shorts, stretching his arms above his head, breathing deeply and ready to go.

Since we arrived, people have been telling us about Nico. The one word that is used repeatedly when they talk about him is 'muscular'. I am looking forward to meeting this muscular Italian but wonder whether a body-builder is the best person to introduce me to Pilates.

He arrives at 8 a.m. Nico is good-looking, with thick curly dark hair, fine features, brown eyes and a six-pack. He is about my height and I guess in his late twenties. He was a professional rugby player, mainly in France, but now lives on the island with his girlfriend and their five-year-old son. He comes from a rich Italian family but finds life in Italy too claustrophobic as the paparazzi tail him all the time.

'If I go out with a man they say I am gay, if I go out with girls they say I have orgies, if I blow my nose they say I am taking coke. Bah, enough, I hate it,' he tells us. Coming from anyone else this would sound ridiculous, but Nico gets away with it. He is extremely likeable, a really 'good man', as Rupert would say. And he oozes energy; he is a real powerhouse. But I don't see what all the muscle chat is about.

'You're from England?' he asks. 'I was sent to England, to Sedbergh, to learn English when I was a teenager. It was a school with NO GIRLS. *Mamma Mia!* I couldn't believe it. I called my parents. Get me out of here, I told them, what is this place?'

Nico started doing Pilates after he did his back in and was told by his doctor that it was either surgery or fix the problem at its base.

'I had heard about Pilates, of course, but I thought it was just mental masturbation,' he says. 'To go from rugby to Pilates, that was a big step. But I did it, and it changed my life.'

We lay out our mats on the lawn close to the swimming pool. The grass is soft and slightly damp; it feels like you're walking on sponges. The sun is already warm but there is a cooling breeze. We look out over the sea. In the foreground there are large frangipani trees with shiny green leaves that contrast against the blue sky and a Santa Maria tree planted in 1956 by British Prime Minister Sir Anthony Eden and his wife.

Nico begins by showing us how to breathe. We fill up our lungs with air, pushing our ribcages out and then breathe out while pushing our belly buttons (or 'belly bottoms', as Nico calls them) towards our spines. In Pilates the breathing is key; it gives you the strength to carry out the exercises, and the other brilliant thing about it is that you basically spend the whole class working your stomach muscles. I find the breathing much easier than the Yoga breathing at La Prairie; in Pilates you breathe in through your nose but out through your mouth.

'Breathe out to the last possible breath,' says Nico. 'And try to visualise that breath. It is the blue of the sky and it is coming out of the top of your head.'

Insane as this sounds, I shut my eyes and do it. The other thing about Pilates that differs so much from regular exercise is that you really have to focus. You go into yourself and concentrate on the breathing in order to get the move right. In that sense you could say that it has a similar meditative effect to yoga.

'The knees are bended,' says Nico, as he takes us through some moves. 'The feets are flat.' His accent is great. Every so often he checks we're in the right position as we breathe out and says, 'Verrrrry gooood.'

Then he whips off his T-shirt, a move I always like in a personal trainer. Good God. I didn't know there were so many muscles in the human torso and every single one is defined. Do I even have all those? And if so, where are they? Unlike me, Nico looks better without his clothes on. He has a very muscular torso but not overworked in a body-builder kind of way, although it's true that his pecs are a little disconcerting.

I'm beginning to really get into this. The Pilates moves feel like they're beneficial; they seem somehow like the sort of moves I should be doing, that go along with my body as opposed to against it, which I often feel when I'm pushing weights or doing sit-ups.

At one stage when I am in the relaxing position (legs bent sitting on haunches, arms out in front) Nico comes and stands over me. 'Inhale,' he says (although it sounds more like 'email'). 'Exhale,' he says, and as I do he pushes down on my back. My whole body relaxes and I sink into a position that must look terribly uncomfortable but feels amazing. My body seems to be telling me that this is good, this is what it wants. I think I'm a convert.

At one stage we come up from a lying position to a sitting position with our arms above our heads, perfect for the stomach muscles. The odd thing is that when I stop focusing for a minute and get the breathing wrong (I breathe in instead of out when making the effort) I don't have the strength to carry out the movement. Pilates is basically about combining deep rhythmic breathing with your movement to get the best out of your body.

We do an exercise called the clam. It basically consists of moving your legs up and down like a clam opening and closing. I am amazed at how hard it is. Being a clam and doing this all day must be exhausting.

'Pilates uses the inner muscles,' explains Nico. 'It works on the core of your body. We use the muscles you can't see, the muscles deep down.'

Pilates was developed by Joseph Pilates, a German of Greek descent (his father was a gymnast) who was a sickly child, suffering from asthma, rickets and rheumatic fever. He dedicated his entire life to becoming physically stronger, beginning his quest as a young boy by studying body-building and gymnastics. In 1912 he moved to England where he earned a living as a boxer, self-defence trainer and circus performer. He was imprisoned during the First World War and it was during his captivity that he developed exercises that bedridden patients could do.

After the war he emigrated to the US and opened his first studio where he taught 'contrology', as he called it, referring to the use of the mind to control the muscles. George Balanchine and Martha Graham were regular students. Joseph Pilates died in 1967 at the age of eighty-seven, having completely overcome his early physical illnesses.

'Pilates develops the body uniformly, corrects wrong postures, restores physical vitality, invigorates the mind and elevates the spirit,' he said. I agree with all of that after just half an hour of it.

In addition Pilates is the perfect exercise to do as we get older. It improves our balance (something we lose with age), improves bone density (thus protecting us from all those horrible ailments of the elderly, such as osteoarthritis, which my mother has), it increases your metabolism (which of course decreases with age), improves muscle tone (so no need to risk side effects by taking human growth hormone to get it back to par), improves your overall mobility by elongating and strengthening the muscles at the same time, it promotes circulation (so no need for woolly socks), it improves posture and flexibility, cures backache within minutes, is good for your joints and, finally, calms your nerves through the deep rhythmic breathing. It is low impact, so everyone can do it; it is the kind of thing you can easily continue into your nineties. Or even start in your nineties. There is a picture of Joe Pilates, aged seventy-five, on the internet. He looks about forty. His muscles are toned and his stomach flat. In fact he looks better than most forty-year-olds I know.

But can this low-impact stretching and breathing be enough to halt the decay of my body? It's all very well finding something I can do into my nineties but what about now? Is this going to reverse the rot and increase my desire to wander around in the buff?

'If you do Pilates at least three times a week, it will be enough to keep you in tone,' says Nico. 'I haven't lifted a weight for ten years. I swim, I do Pilates and I do press-ups. Every morning I wake up and I do my Pilates and press-ups routine to keep in shape, then I also swim. The cardiovascular is important as we get older, otherwise we can die of a heart attack.'

So rather like there's no point in having no wrinkles if you have Alzheimer's, there's no point having a taut body and then keeling over from thrombosis.

But how about keeping something like your breasts in shape, I ask Nico, admiring his pecs. How would you do that?

'Press-ups,' he says. 'You do it with your hands close together on the floor.' He shows me and I try to copy him. I collapse on the mat.

'You have to build up your strength,' he says. 'Do one on the first day, two on the third day, three on the fifth day and so forth. I do one hundred, five sets of twenty, in between the Pilates moves.'

Nico proceeds to tell us that he is not in his late twenties as I first thought. He is in fact forty. I have to say he looks absolutely incredible. I ask him the secret of his success.

'Exercise and diet,' he says.

Just as Carolyn's Facial Fitness is a natural alternative to Botox and fillers, Nico's anti-ageing method for the body is a natural alternative to liposuction and tummy tucks.

Just looking at him makes me think that it really is possible at least to slow the ageing process down to almost a standstill, and you don't even have to make yourself miserable doing it. This is a man who has clearly never seen a needle or a cannula, but looks twenty years younger than he is. OK, so some of it is bound to be genetic. But as Tina Richards says, if you smoke and sit in the sun constantly then ageing is inevitable. What Nico is doing is basically almost eliminating the environmental ageing factors. He lives such a healthy life that if his genes are good (and by the look of him they are) he should look like he does today for at least another fifteen years. And even then I can't imagine him ageing badly.

Of course he does have the advantage of living in Jamaica, with a pool at his disposal, and his job is doing Pilates overlooking the sea. His lifestyle is one that most of us can only dream of. Exercising for him is easy, it is part of his daily routine, but that's partly because he doesn't have to commute to work or sit in an office for twelve hours a day. Having said that, Nico has always exercised, wherever he was living. In Paris he would go jogging at four o'clock in the morning, in order to avoid the worst of the pollution.

I certainly won't be getting up at four in the morning to do Pilates, but I will add some Pilates moves to my daily early morning sun salute routine and I will also do the breast-enhancing press-ups at least three times a week. And one day I might even have breasts as big as Nico's.

I knew I would be mad about Pilates; I just don't know why it took me so long to get on to it. What has most surprised me, though, is my husband's conversion. He too is mad about it and has vowed to carry on. He's even talking about finding a class near us and buying Pilates DVDs.

'According to a website I looked at we'll notice a big difference after six weeks,' I tell him after a couple of sessions with Nico.

'I've noticed a difference after three hours,' he says optimistically.

Thinking back to my stress level, I do notice a dramatic improvement here. Already the view out of the vast window in the bedroom at the Fleming Villa makes me feel relaxed. Two trees (Jamaican almonds) on either side of a round table in a sunken garden, shaped like large parasols, have met up in the middle, providing shade for the table, and their thick green juicy leaves intermingle so you no longer know which leaves belong to which tree. From the trunks delicate flowers spout, not part of the tree, but beautiful pink parasites that have chosen the trees as their home. Beyond the trees is the sea. It goes on for miles, culminating in a perfectly straight horizon, gently moving along, rhythmically carrying endless waves to the private beach below. The rolling hills around my mother's house in Devon have the same feeling of peace.

I wish I could take the view with me.

Back home I find the smallest thing sends me into a stress; from a traffic jam to a shoe going missing (actually, that's not small) to trying to find the children's judo kit. This is something I have to control if I don't want to die of a heart attack (though genetically unlikely according to my gene test) or age prematurely. Since we arrived in Jamaica a week ago, I haven't lost my temper once. At home if I don't end up shouting at someone at least four times a day I consider it a triumph. Here I have not been stressed and I do look a lot better than I did when we arrived. My skin is smoother, my eyes clearer, I would say I look at least three years younger than the woman who stepped off the plane. Such a shame that Colin Firth lookalike isn't around now.

But obviously this is away from home, away from the everyday stresses of my daily routine. Instead of looking at a pile of ironing I am looking at the sea, instead of my washing up and cooking, a nice little man arrives an hour before every meal and asks me if I'd like it in the sunken garden, at the beach or in the gazebo.

But it must be possible to minimise stress at home. My mother says that when she's in a traffic jam instead of thinking, Oh bugger, I'm going to be late, she thinks, How brilliant, I have some time to myself to think about whatever I like. A friend of mine says the minute something stressful happens she starts to breathe deeply. I have tried that but it only lasts about a second. However, now that I am a Pilates convert I will breathe rhythmically instead of hyperventilating.

What I might also try to do is to remember the view out of the window here and think about that as opposed to the annoying person in the queue in front of me making me late, the overdraft or the vast pile of ironing I need to get through. Or even the giant wrinkle in the middle of my forehead.

CHAPTER NINE

My First Anti-Ageing Conference

What do I wear to a party where all the men will be wearing Lycra? I am in London to continue my anti-ageing quest and have found myself in anti-ageing heaven. Or hell, depending on how you look at it: an anti-ageing conference. But apart from attending the conference, I am here to meet my husband, who is arriving this afternoon on a bicycle from France.

This is not something he does on a regular basis or as a cheap way to get to London; he is raising money for the Shooting Star Children's Hospice. Later on today, the nine cyclists will ride into Elgin Grove in a blaze of glory and I will join the other doting wives and girl-friends to greet them.

But before that I have a lot of work to do at the second annual anti-ageing conference organised by

Heather Bird Health, the Beauchamp Place-based health and beauty clinic where I did my gene-testing. First I need an outfit for both anti-ageing experts and cyclists. I opt for jeans, high heels and a black top. High heels always make you look younger, it's a well-known fact that the infirm can't walk in them. And you can't go wrong in black; at least it won't clash with the Lycra.

The conference is being held at the Royal Society of Medicine in Wimpole Street. On my way there I try to imagine what sort of people will attend an anti-ageing conference. Will it be full of desperate women of a certain age looking for the secret of eternal youth (like me)? Or dermatologists and doctors trying to learn about the latest techniques so they can take them back to their practices and make a fortune?

The answer is some of all of the above. The auditorium has around 250 red leather chairs, quite plush and comfortable. The place is half full or half empty, depending on your perception. I would say a glass is half full, for example. Carla would always say half empty. 'Otherwise you can't fill it up,' she argues. There are lots of professional-looking types and, rather oddly, at least twenty platinum blondes. George Best's ex-wife Angie, is among them, sitting next to another B-list celebrity, Rula Lenska. I am told by the woman sitting next to me, a doctor from Harrogate, that Cherie Blair's health guru is here. I try to work out which one she is. Maybe the one with the ridiculous blonde hair extensions that make her look like she's wearing an Afghan Hound on her head? Or the petite woman in front of me with badly dyed red hair and a rather eccentric cream suit, which seems to be having an identity crisis over which material it should be made out of: silk, lace or wool? It's not a good look. Or maybe it's the Harrogate doctor herself, double bluffing so she doesn't end up exposed in the *Daily Mail*.

There is a stage with a podium to the right of it. Heather Bird, the organiser, is standing there ready to open the conference. She looks picture perfect, almost like a Barbie doll; there is no other way to describe her. She has long, flaxen hair, she is super-thin, she's wearing a Chanel suit (pink with black trimmings) and her skin is perfectly smooth. She is tanned and has nice, wide blue eyes. When she starts to speak, rather touchingly, she seems quite nervous. She also arrives with a baby, which she hands to a handsome younger man standing next to her.

'Good choice of nanny,' I whisper to my neighbour.

'That's not her nanny,' snaps my neighbour. 'That's her bodyguard.'

Even better.

'Why does she have a bodyguard?'

'She's worth millions, married to the owner of some supermarket chain.'

Heather introduces the first speaker. He is a Professor Inre Zs-Nagy, an expert in Growth Hormone Replacement Therapy from the Department of Geriatrics at the University of Budapest. I love the idea of a whole department of geriatrics; I imagine corridors filled with people on Zimmer frames and a lunchroom with only grey heads tucking into their borscht.

Professor Zs-Nagy would fit in well. Probably because, as he admits to us, he has never tried growth hormone replacement. He tells me later that he couldn't afford it before as it was too expensive. Now that prices have come down he can, and it's just a question of finding the right time.

I have come across the idea of it before. It is one of those things you get sent spam about. The ones offering me a bigger penis I never open (mine's big enough, thank you) but I did open an email from a certain Cody Fowler, which told me how my body could benefit in all sorts of ways from hGH or human growth hormone. I could boost my immune system, increase my sex drive (maybe that bigger willy might come in useful, after all), look and feel younger, revitalise my heart, liver, kidney and lungs and sleep soundly. Of all of the above it was the last one that most interested me, as I believe that if I sleep well all the rest will follow; but as the reason I don't sleep is three small children waking me up I didn't think hGH could help me.

But the way Professor Zs-Nagy talks about it, I might have to reconsider. He tells us it is the key to longevity and a youthful body. That we could change our appearance and our health with a few injections. Put simply, the hormone stimulates growth and cell reproduction.

It is created in the frontal part of the pituitary gland and is a protein-like hormone that is chemically quite similar to insulin. During childhood growth hormone controls growth, and children with a deficiency used to reach adulthood as dwarfs. As we age, our natural growth hormones decrease, although levels remain stable for several decades. Men and women over fifty usually have levels ranging from 150 down to as low as 30 or even less. By the time we're sixty our levels are 75 per cent less than they are in the average twenty-five-year-old. The idea with this treatment is to get back up to the levels we had when we were young, thereby making us fitter, stronger and, ultimately, younger again.

According to an article in the *New England Journal*

of Medicine the stuff they sell on the internet is no good. 'Since growth hormone is a peptide subject to degradation by gastric acid, oral preparations would not be expected to be effective.' In other words, if you swallow it, it won't work, and the ones sold on the net are usually sold in the form of pills. To work it has to be injected.

Elmer Cranton, author of the book *Resetting the Clock*, maintains that many of the problems we encounter in old age are 'a deficiency state, much like a vitamin deficiency. As we age, we develop age-related hormonal deficiencies.' He claims that with hormones he can 'turn people's lives around'.

A friend of mine in New York who has Aids has a fridge stuffed with human growth hormone. He says his friends are always coming round, trying to steal it.

'I can't take too much of it,' he says. 'It makes my heart race.'

And therein lies one of the problems with hGH. According to some schools of thought it 'speeds' up your organs, thus actually directly contributing to an earlier death. So although you might feel better, you might die sooner.

At the conference I run into Dr Jennifer Krup, a hormone expert. She is American, very sassily dressed in a cream and black suit, has short blonde hair, cut well, and subtle make-up. She has tried hGH. 'To be honest I didn't notice a lot of difference,' she tells me. 'But that was because I was so miserable due to lack of oestrogen and progesterone. And it's a lot of money: around £120 a week.'

'I would say you can sometimes get better results through lifestyle changes than injections,' she says. She explains that there are other ways to stimulate hGH that are probably better for you in the long run, like exercise, and especially weight training.

'Try to do at least an hour a day, even if it's just walking,' she says. 'You should also eat better and sleep better. In terms of anti-ageing the number-one thing a physician can help you with is hormones. There is no need to feel below par just because you're reaching the menopause. Get yourself checked out and get your hormones balanced.'

Dr Krup is, of course, not the only doctor to advocate Hormone Replacement Therapy. According to Dr Jeya Prakash, a clinical doctor based in Harley Street, hormones are the most essential element to anti-ageing. 'But you must treat them like an orchestra,' he says. 'Don't just look at a single one. Every instrument is important, otherwise it is like just feeling the elephant's tail and saying it is an elephant.'

I ask Dr Krup about the risks of HRT.

'There are risks; of course, the main risk is breast cancer,' she says.

'What else?'

'Cholesterol,' she says. 'It increases with age and we don't know why. It's from having the wrong mother and father; if you come from the UK then you are at a higher risk. One in two women die from heart attacks in the UK. Yes, I can fix your hormones but you will look very good in your coffin if you don't get your cholesterol under control.'

'What do you think of Botox and treatments like that?'

'I've done Botox and will carry on doing Botox,' she says. 'I had a wrinkle right here,' she points to the middle of her brow, 'that always made me look very angry. Now I don't have it any more.'

'You're not worried that it's a poison?' I ask.

'I also colour my hair, which is a poison, and I dread to think about the lipstick I have swallowed over the decades. The air that I'm breathing out there can't possibly be good for me either.'

Fair point, I suppose.

'Anyway,' she continues, 'you're miles away from hormone replacement. How old are you?'

'Thirty-eight,' I lie. As far as I'm concerned lying about my age is one of the most effective ways to stay young.

I have been lying about my age since I can remember and it's a habit that is hard to break. I even lie to my children about my age. Recently Olivia asked me if a man had ever walked on the moon. I told her about Neil Armstrong.

'Wow, really?' she said. 'Is that true? Well, it must be, I know you wouldn't lie to me.' She paused. 'Well, only about your age.'

At least with Dr Krup I am closer to the truth than normal. When my book about French women was seri-alised in the *Daily Mail* I told them I was thirty-five, on the advice of a publicist. My mother thought it was a typo. 'It's a lovely article, darling, but they seem to think you're thirty-five,' she said.

One old admirer called to check that I had in fact given them the wrong age.

'Thank God for that,' he said when I confirmed that I had knocked a few years off. 'I was beginning to worry that I was a complete pervert all those years ago.'

The awful thing about lying about your age is that once you start, where do you stop? I even lied to my friend Mary when I first met her. That was before we became really close. One day she said to me: 'You know you look really good for thirty-eight.' I felt like a total worm. But it wasn't until six months later when I finally confessed. She took it in her stride. 'You silly thing,' she said. 'What's wrong with being older? It's not like you haven't achieved anything.'

I suppose the achievement thing is part of the lying thing. I remember when my husband hit thirty-seven, he spent the whole day depressed because he had just realised that by the time Byron was his age he'd already been dead for a year. My aunt always says that if someone hasn't achieved anything by the time they're forty, they never will. This may have been true when she was forty but I don't think it's a valid argument these days.

My father and aunt never tell anyone how old they are so I once asked them how to tackle the issue without lying. My aunt suggested skirting around the question of age by changing the subject.

'But what if someone asks you outright how old you are?' I said.

'Say "about your age" and then walk away,' said my father. 'Anyone who asks that question deserves to be ignored.'

I leave Dr Krup and wander into the main room where people are already gathering for lunch. It is a light, airy space with a marble floor and chairs dotted about. The loos downstairs are the smartest I have seen outside a five-star hotel. The RSM's modern interior is a contrast to its façade, which is reassuringly old-fashioned: one of those Victorian buildings that could only be in London. I suppose most people in the room are after the opposite effect.

One of them is a mad woman. Well, she's not actually mad – at least I don't think she is – she is actually very nice, but she is all about auras and rather the opposite to most of the other people at the conference, who are there to make money, as far as I can make out.

'My approach to anti-ageing is to connect to the earth and sky energies and channel my energy,' says the aura lady. 'I'm fifty now and eight years ago I was a crack cocaine addict.'

Right.

She tells me how she was working for a Japanese financial institution and made her first million aged thirty-two. 'I was psychologically bankrupt,' she tells me. 'Emotionally dead. I worshipped at the altar of Prada, Gucci and Chanel.'

Sounds great to me.

'I was bored so I started doing drugs,' she continues, now looking all homely and healthy in a long flowing kaftan-style garment. Her hair is completely grey, but glossy and thick and rather nicely cut in a bob.

She tries to explain what it is that has changed so radically in her life but I find it hard to get my head round it. It all seems to be linked to auras and energies. 'You learn to wake up and become conscious,' she says. 'Working with energy, your whole life changes. You tend to stay well and to stop ageing.'

'So you don't need Botox any more?'

'I don't agree with Botox because you're basically saying only one idea of beauty exists. Why should we all try and look like Kate Moss?'

'So how do you use these energies?'

'You use your brain to be able to tune into the various energies,' she explains. 'Look, I've never had surgery. I did enough damage to myself to destroy myself. I used to shake all over, I pulled all of my hair out. But when I had that divine intervention, that electromagnetic experience, it absolutely changed my life. All disease and ageing comes from stress. When we can eradicate fear and stress from our lives we can reverse the ageing process. Toxic thoughts and feelings, toxic lifestyles, keep us separate from love and cause stress and fear and tension in our lives that cause ageing.'

I think it all sounds great. I mean, it makes sense

that stress is bad and if we can channel our energy positively as opposed to negatively that's all good. But, to be honest it's a little too vague for me. How will all this energy stuff help with my wrinkle? I need something concrete, something I can use and then see the results in a mirror. I'm all for a bit of spirituality but my face needs more drastic measures.

Heather Bird Health, the conference organisers, have a stand on which they show all the treatments they do. During my quest so far I have experienced surgery (second-hand), facials, yoga, massages, a stress-free existence and being wrapped in seaweed. But what is really beginning to interest me is the power of the needle.

I arrange to interview Heather Bird herself after the conference. She looks great and runs an anti-ageing clinic, so she must be able to tell me more.

We meet at her clinic in Beauchamp Place. As soon as I walk in I am ushered to the bar and given a smoothie with a wheatgrass chaser. This is good news because the night before, I was drinking chasers of another kind to celebrate my husband's safe arrival in Elgin Grove, so I'm feeling terrible.

Heather wafts in, looking healthy and glamorous. I

immediately want to give up on life or at least never touch alcohol again.

Rather endearingly, Heather wasn't always so bleeding perfect. 'I took a test and found I was thirteen years over my chronological age,' she tells me. 'So I decided to take action.' At the time she was hanging out in Tramps nightclub a lot, drinking and partying, not smoking herself but in the company of smokers (including her husband).

'What a ride that was,' she says laughing. 'But when I took the test I stopped going to nightclubs. It's essential to get your sleep as that's when your hormones rebalance. When I was out partying I was up until 3 or 4 a.m. and drinking alcohol every night, because if you don't drink you just can't sit and watch everyone else. Now I eat 75 per cent raw food. I love salads. I was a person who ate meat every day. When you start eating healthily it feeds upon itself; you enjoy and crave that sort of food; there's nothing better for me now than a huge organic salad.'

Heather was born in Salt Lake City and brought up as a Mormon, although she converted to Judaism when she married Robert Tchenguiz. She says her intention was always to choose a livelihood that would contribute, so medicine was a natural choice.

'I started witnessing first-hand the degenerative

effects of ageing,' she says. 'I saw the results of Alzheimer's, strokes, illnesses. I had to move patients into wheelchairs, change their nappies and everything. I was so young and at an age when you think you are always going to be young, but then I realised that how you age depends on how you live and this helped to define my mission. I started out with the intention of becoming a doctor to help people, but soon realised that I would impact and contribute more to the world if instead of being a doctor I used my business acumen and my vision to spread the news of preventative medicine through medical practitioners working in clinics around the world and through medical conferences.'

Heather's mission is to change our 'fix-it mentality'. She came to England because that is where she saw the greatest need. 'The mentality here is to wait until it's really broken and then go fix it on the NHS,' she says. 'I am in for the long haul; I am interested in the long-term, in educating people, in raising their level of awareness.'

She describes the clinics she runs (one in Beauchamp Place and another in Wimpole Street) as 'medical' but there are also a great deal of beauty treatments available.

'I have to find a way to get people to take care of themselves and if that means appealing to their vanity then I will do that,' she says.

But she is not only in it for the glory. 'I am a business person and want to make money,' she says. 'I really want this business to work.' Plus 10 per cent of all her earnings go to the Mormons.

'Why is looking good so important to women?' I ask her.

'Not just to women,' she answers. 'It's becoming more so for men. My husband is a big businessman; I see what businessmen are doing to keep the cutting edge, to stop the young guns overtaking them. They want to keep their hair, they want to keep their testosterone levels up, they want to keep fit; they're doing Botox as well.'

Heather does look very young. She tells me she is thirty-nine. I would have guessed mid-thirties. So is she still thirteen years over her chronological age?

'No, I'm now down to four years over.'

I want to put her theories to the test, so Heather suggests I try something called mesotherapy with anti-ageing bioflush. Sounds great. I am taken upstairs to the treatment room and introduced to a man with an indefinable accent and an unpronounceable name. 'We just call him Dr Miracle,' says Tina, the nurse.

Dr Miracle is tall, bordering on lanky, with a mop of blond hair and several mobile phones, which he answers in various languages, stuffed into his white coat.

Mesotherapy literally means treating the area itself as opposed to taking a pill or, if you're French, putting something up your bottom. Dr Miracle is preparing a needle filled with hyaluronic acid and a concoction of anti-ageing vitamins and antioxidants to inject into my skin.

'Your skin will look fresh, rejuvenated and take on a youthful appearance,' says Tina as she shows me where to lie down. 'Fine lines will disappear, and it's a natural product reabsorbed back into the body.'

'Is it as effective as Botox?' I ask, hoping Dr Miracle will say yes. Botox has already become a word that causes an involuntary reaction in me. I am scared and intrigued by the idea in equal measure.

'No, but it is a good alternative. Lots of people still find the idea of Botox too scary.'

'At what age should one start this treatment?' I wonder if it's already too late for me.

'It is really aimed to be preventative,' says Dr Miracle. 'You can use it aged twenty, thirty or forty and upwards.'

'How often?'

'First do a series of three treatments and then a top-up every six months or so. I have some clients who are actresses and come in every month,' he says. 'They look great.'

'Where should you have it? Just on the face?' I ask,

wondering if I can improve my body while I'm here as well.

'It works brilliantly on the hands, neck and décolletage as well. I find that people start with the face and then want it all over.'

'And it really makes a difference?' I can't quite believe that sticking a needle with a substance into my neck or hands is going to rejuvenate them overnight.

Dr Miracle leaps from his chair. 'On an older face it really does,' he enthuses. 'If you're fifty or sixty you can lose five to ten years in one session.'

'And the side effects? The downsides?'

'It can be a little bit painful and so we use an anaesthetic cream, which can sometimes cause a reaction.'

'When you say painful, how painful?'

'We use an acupuncture-sized needle so really not painful at all. But I can give you some anaesthetic cream if you'd like some?'

'No, I'll be fine,' I tell him. Most women would walk over hot coals to get rid of fine lines and look younger. I would do a lot more. A little bit of pain is really not an issue.

Dr Miracle prepares his needle. 'I am going to be injecting you over one thousand times,' he tells me. 'I will focus on the areas I think you need it most. I will begin to erase your wrinkles.'

Suddenly I feel ready to weep. 'Thank you,' I whimper gratefully and close my eyes.

'I use Botox, fillers, lasers, everything,' he goes on. 'With mesotherapy 95 per cent come back for more. And the brilliant thing is, it's not a burning laser treatment, it's completely natural.'

'So what does it actually do?'

'I inject the hyaluronic acid into the deepest layer of the skin,' he explains as he works the needle expertly and extremely quickly over my entire face. 'I put these moisture molecules under the skin so they cannot escape, unlike a face cream. There are no marks, you can go out immediately, but it's even better the day after. Your skin will be like silk.'

He hovers over my mouth area. 'I will do a lot here,' he says. 'But this can be the painful part. What do you think about your lips, why don't you like them?'

'What do you mean?'

'Are they too little, what do you think? Just if I broaden them out it will give you good appearance, not something artificial, of course.'

'I'll bear it in mind,' I say, secretly wishing he could just inject something into them then and there to transform me. This is the dangerous thing about lying in a treatment room like this one at HB Health. You are told what a difference all this will make and you actually begin to believe it. Already I am a mesotherapy addict and I have yet to see the results.

'Do you believe women should have face-lifts or is there so much else out there now we don't need to any more?' I ask Dr Miracle.

'If you can avoid surgery then you should,' he says. 'But most important – start to think about yourself, about diet, exercise, how to live better, how to be healthy. Now, we're finished. Take a look.'

I walk over to the mirror and look into it. My skin is glowing. I look like I've been for a walk in the rain. I look fresh, young and sparkling. I smile.

'You see, you see!' Dr Miracle is hopping around behind me. 'I told you it was brilliant. Your skin looks shiny, touch it, it's amazing.'

I do as he says. Actually, I look like I've had a good night's sleep. I tell him so.

'No, you look like you've had two good nights' sleep,' he says, gazing into my pores. 'And maybe I could do just a little on the lips? If you want to see me again?'

'I'd love to see you again,' I tell him, looking at my new complexion. 'When?'

CHAPTER TEN

An Encounter with a Laser

That's it. Either that wrinkle goes or I do. It has been annoying me for months but has now taken on gigantic proportions. It sits there smugly, right in the middle of my forehead. No amount of facials, mesotherapy or exfoliating will budge it. It is there, like a monument to the fact that I am no longer twenty-five, or even thirty-five. I hate it more than I have ever hated anything about myself, bar perhaps my caesarean scar but at least with that I got baby Bea. What the hell has this wrinkle ever done for me? Well, we're about to fall out, big time.

I make an appointment with Dr Patrick Bowler, who runs the Court House Clinic. He achieved TV fame with a series called *Ten Years Younger* and has written a book called *The Nervous Girl's Guide to Nip 'n' Tuck*. I am going to see him to ask him how he can help me in my anti-ageing quest.

I arrange to meet him on the hottest day in England since records began. It is a strange feeling, wandering around the streets of London, frying and ready to dive in a cold shower. No one talks about anything except the weather, so no change there. The first problem I run into is that the clinic is not on Wimpole Street, as its address suggests, it is on New Cavendish Street. So I run around for ten minutes with all my luggage (I am heading off to Devon after this meeting, where my children are staying with my mother) getting sweatier and grumpier by the minute. Saying something is on one street when it's not is one of those peculiarly English things, a bit like the French filling their words with letters they don't bother to pronounce.

Once I find the right place, I ring the buzzer. I am looking forward to getting inside some cool, clean, white surroundings, as I imagine his clinic will be. A mixture between a Swiss hospital and a beauty salon. A shrill noise opens the door. There is no air conditioning and the décor is blue, a rather murky blue.

I explain to the receptionist that I have come to meet Dr Bowler and also Priti Patel, the clinic manager, who is going to show me around. Good name for a woman in the beauty industry. The receptionist asks me to take a seat and answers a ringing phone. A woman in a pink suit walks towards the door, her face more or less the same colour as her jacket; I suspect she's had some peeling treatment or other.

I have been very excited about this meeting. It was Mary who first spotted Dr Bowler on TV and suggested I go to see him. She even suggested she go instead of me. After four children she feels she's in need of a little pepping up.

'But you won't know what to ask,' I tell her.

'Don't be so selfish,' she replies.

Priti Patel arrives and says she'll show me around before I am ushered in to meet the great man. We go to a consulting room where two of the therapists are chatting. The clinic offers a variety of anti-ageing treatments such as chemical peels, microdermabrasion and Botox. Priti's favourite is the Omnilux Revive, which delivers a natural method of light-only skin rejuvenation using red and infrared light. It's all to do with something called LEDs (light-emitting diodes).

Basically what they do is soften fine lines, improve skin tone and leave you with smooth skin. Clare Robson, one of the therapists, says it's an ideal thing to have before a big event, like a wedding.

I ask Clare what the difference is between the sorts of treatments they do and the ones on offer at beauty salons, such as the facial I had in Paris.

'Basically everything they have in a beauty salon you can get here,' she says. 'But it's more medical and more effective. I have clients who now come to us instead of going to a salon.'

Clare is with another therapist, who is twenty-five and about to have Botox on some non-existent wrinkles on her forehead.

'It's more of a preventative measure,' she tells me.

I am still suspicious of Botox. The first thing that makes me suspicious is the idea that you're injecting poison into your body. Surely this can't be a good thing. Also, I have a friend who said her eyelids drooped afterwards and she had to have corrective surgery. I ask Clare if she has seen any horror stories. No, she tells me, not in the three and a half years she has been working for Dr Bowler.

'I've even had it myself,' she adds. 'Under my arms.'

'What's wrong with your underarms?' I ask her, craning my neck to take a look.

'I had Botox to prevent excessive sweating,' she tells me.

On the hottest day since records began, she does look remarkably cool.

I would not consider having Botox under my arms but I did have the hair under my arms lasered. It was hugely expensive, around £500. When I told Carla she was horrified. I made her promise not to tell Rupert.

'I cannot believe the price you are about to pay to have your underarms lasered,' she wrote to me. 'Tell me this is a joke. I will trim them with my teeth for half the price (but draw line at bikini). Of course I shall tell Rupert, he will be eternally grateful to me and invite me to stay every Christmas with Tia.'

I didn't take her up on her kind offer but went ahead with the laser treatment. It was worth every penny. After four sessions it was all done. I never need to shave there again. And Carla didn't tell Rupert.

'So is it better to have Botox, or peels and other treatments like the light treatment?' I now ask Clare.

'Both. Botox is different and if you have it here our policy is to give you a minimal amount and offer a free top-up in two weeks' time to see what effect it's had. A lot of disasters come about when people don't think it's made a difference, but it can take up to two weeks to show. My advice, though, is that if you have Botox you should look after your skin in other ways by, for example, having peels or light treatment.'

While I wait to see Dr Bowler I reflect on what I've

just seen. I think there is something quite odd about someone aged twenty-five having Botox. I mean, if you can't relax and enjoy being young at that age when can you? At twenty-five I was still drinking and smoking way too much without a thought about how to prevent ageing. Ageing just hadn't occurred to me. It was still something that happened to other people.

And I certainly don't remember when my first wrinkle appeared, or when *the* wrinkle I am now intent on destroying reared its ugly head.

The odd thing is that I really feel no different now from when I was at university and, as far as I can make out from others, this won't change. My mother-in-law, who is in her seventies, says she often catches sight of herself in the mirror and thinks, Oh, help, who is that poor old grey-haired dear, and then realises it's her. As Germaine Greer says: 'Passing a shop window you see yourself walking, and realise you locomote in old-lady mode . . . You become more and more aware of the possibility of falling; on rain-slick pavements and polished floors you shuffle. Soon you will find yourself shuffling full time.'

Of course if you take two women of a similar age and compare them they may age totally differently. Some of this will be down to genetics and some down to lifestyle, but according to Carla, who recently went to a school reunion, how you age is also determined by how you were as a child. At least in her experience those who were more confident, attractive and out-going as children have remained so. Those who were shy and unpopular are now grey-haired and dressed like dowdy matrons. The more popular girls now look ten years younger, at least. Sadly it seems that life's winners remain life's winners.

I am ushered in to Dr Bowler's office. As soon as I sit down he grabs a round light with a glass tube from behind him, lights it and shines it on my face. He has a murderous look in his eyes. I hope he's looking at my most-hated wrinkle. But no.

'How much sun exposure have you had?' he asks.

I feel like a prisoner being interrogated. 'Well, I do live in the south of France.'

'Do you use sunscreen?' he continues, peering at my pores. 'Do you wear a hat?'

I have to admit that until I started researching this book sunscreen was not one of those things I went out and looked for. I have olive skin and don't really burn, so it always seemed like something I could do without. However, I fear Dr Bowler might hit me on the head with his light if I admit this so I say that I do when I go out into the sun. I avoid the hat issue. The last time I wore one was to Royal Ascot about ten years ago. It was lovely, pink and rather large, and made it impossible to see where I was going.

'Hmm.' He sounds sceptical. 'Let's have a closer look. Raise your eyebrows, please.'

I do as he says.

'Would you say that frowning is a family trait?'

He's obviously spotted *the* wrinkle. I knew it was only a matter of time.

'Yes, in fact my mother frowns in her sleep.'

'Let me have a look at the backs of your hands,' he says, shining his light on them.

'What do you think?' I ask, and add, only half-jokingly, 'A full face-lift immediately? I don't want to look any older than this.'

'You've had far too much exposure to the sun,' he says. 'But you've inherited a good skin colour so it could be a lot worse than it is. If you were a red-haired person with very fair skin you would probably be going into your forties looking sixty with the amount of sun you've had, but luckily for you, you're not.'

'What about this wrinkle?' I ask, pointing at my nemesis.

'That could easily be Botoxed. The bottom half of your face isn't bad at all. I would suggest Botox across the forehead and around the eyes.'

'How many injections are we talking about here?'

'I would say four or five across the forehead and two or three around the eyes.'

'How much will it cost?'

'We charge by the area. £200 for one area. £60 for any subsequent area. So all that lot would cost you £320.'

I am tempted, but still wary.

'I heard about a colleague of mine who ended up with a shelf instead of a forehead,' I say. 'Do you see many disasters?'

'Not many,' he says. 'But when I do see them they come from things like Botox parties. There are no regulations in the UK at the moment, so you have to be careful about who you go to. I would say that 99 per cent of my patients are after a natural look. They don't want people to say, "Who did your Botox?" they want people to say, "You look good." Also there is no point in giving a sixty-year-old the smooth forehead of a thirty-year-old. It would look ridiculous.'

'But once you start Botox, don't you just have to keep going all the time?'

'About three times a year should be enough,' says

Dr Bowler. 'That's how often I inject myself. I used to have terrible lines.'

'So Botox would help with this wrinkle?' I ask, pointing at my most hated one.

'Yes, it would, and you might even find that it acts as a preventative measure and stops it from getting any deeper. The fact is if you hinder the muscle movement with Botox, then the wrinkles don't get deeper. I would say most of my patients are aged between forty and fifty but I have seen an increasing amount of patients in their late twenties coming on for treatments to prevent wrinkles developing in the first place.'

This is sounding more and more interesting.

'Have you ever thought about having any fillers?' asks Dr Bowler.

Charming. Fillers give your face volume where it is starting to sag, droop or look generally old, for example in the creases around your nose, or your lips. They are responsible for many horrendous trout-pouts. If you are considering a trout-pout or at least a minnow-pout, then I suggest you go for a filler that your body can break down instead of silicone, which is permanent, so if your pout is too trouty you're stuck with it.

Aside from my own worries about injecting my face with poison, I have another problem with Botox and fillers and so on. Rupert is completely set against it. He has tried very hard to keep me on the natural ageing track throughout the research I have done so far for this book. He hates anything fake. 'If you ever have surgery I'll divorce you,' he once told me.

I'm not about to have surgery but I have a nagging suspicion that Botox and fillers might fall under the same umbrella. His argument is that it's just not necessary and it shows a rather vain and stupid side to women he doesn't like. He's annoyed me a bit by constantly telling me he's sure I'm going to do it. 'It's only a matter of time before you fall for Botox,' he says, shaking his head knowingly every few days. 'I bet you'll do it.' So I want to prove him wrong. If I do end up doing anything, at the very least, it will have to be subtle.

'What else could I do?' I ask Dr Bowler. 'Something that doesn't involve needles.'

'You could do some treatments like chemical peels, IPL treatments or microdermabrasion.'

IPL treatments are intense pulsed light treatments, which are very good for improving your overall skin tone and boosting collagen growth. Microdermabrasion is like an intense facial, which removes dead skin cells as well as stimulating the growth of elastic fibres and collagen. Chemical peels are slightly more drastic. This basically involves putting acid on your face and peeling off the skin. There are some that are mild but some can take the skin right down to the muscles. Then you have to stay at home for three weeks while it grows back. Apparently the results are amazing but I'm not prepared to try it just yet. It sounds a little too violent. And not particularly subtle.

Other treatments that Dr Bowler talks about in his book include lasers that resurface or plump the skin, red light treatments that improve the condition of the skin and increase cell activity, microsclerotherapy for treating little thread and spider veins, and radiofrequency treatments for tightening the skin and reducing cellulite.

'This is all very well but in truth you can't really halt the ageing process, can you?' I ask.

'No, but we can slow it down.'

'And where does it all stop? When do you say enough is enough? When do you change from zapping your wrinkles to welcoming them?'

'I had an eighty-four-year-old lady in here a while back who wanted a tummy tuck. She said she had spent all her life looking after her husband and children and now she wanted to do something for herself.'

'Did you do it?'

'No, luckily her medical condition precluded her from having an operation,' he says. 'But you see, to her it was still important. It would have been very rude of me to say, "You're eighty-four – who on earth is going to look at your tummy now?"'

'Why do you think people are becoming more and more obsessed with staying young-looking?'

'I think for women it boils down to confidence. If they look better, they feel better about themselves. But there are a lot of things that precipitate coming here, such as hitting forty, a divorce; all sorts of factors. And I think the media makes people more aware and perhaps question whether they should be having stuff done as everyone else is. Of course, it used to be that just the rich and famous could do this kind of thing. Now having Botox is like having your hair done.'

'But a lot of these celebs go a bit overboard, don't they? I mean, is it just me or does Dolly Parton look mad?'

'I feel sorry for these people,' he says. 'Their face and body is their fortune so maybe they feel duty-bound to do all this stuff, but they can end up looking like a person suffering from body dysmorphia, someone who just keeps having surgery and is never satisfied.'

I ask him what most people come to have done.

'For women it's the lines around the eyes, for men the frown lines. Unless they're really bad they can all be treated with Botox.'

'What about this flappy bit on top of my eyelid – how could you treat that?' I ask, showing him the loose skin I spend hours trying to smooth out.

'That looks like a family trait to me and it doesn't need doing at the moment, but when the time comes it would be surgery.'

'And stretch marks?' I ask, partly for myself but also on behalf of Mary, who has sent me to London with a list of questions.

'Where are they?' he asks.

'On my bottom,' I say, half-standing up before I decide against pulling my pants down. He knows what a stretch mark looks like, for heaven's sake.

'There's nothing we can do for that at the moment,' he says.

Stretch marks are one of the most difficult things to treat. The best thing is, of course, to avoid getting them at all, but as genes often determine that it can be tricky. Throughout all my pregnancies I rubbed myself with oil every day. But sadly, rapid weight loss and gain have left me with some marks. And now they're there they won't budge. Laser treatments are definitely the way forward when it comes to erasing stretch marks, and there has been some progress, notably in the US, where dermatologists treat them with a machine called the Titan, but with limited results.

So I decide to focus on my face instead, before it's too late, and take him up on his kind offer of an Omnilux Revive, their most popular anti-ageing treatment outside injectables. It costs £55 a session and involves my face being pounded with a red light, which stimulates the fibroblast cells to produce collagen, which in turn softens fine lines and improves skin tone. It is good for general skin condition and rejuvenation. Ideally you should have a series of nine treatments twice a week over a month.

The microdermabrasion is done with a machine with tiny diamonds that take off the dead layer of skin. It feels a little uncomfortable at times so it must be doing me some good. The red light treatment is heavenly, though. I feel all warm and cosy; it must be great on a cold winter's day. Afterwards my skin looks and feels smooth and clear. Almost as good as after my mesotherapy session. I also had a good sleep during the treatment or at least I would have done if the Antipodean beautician hadn't kept asking me if I was OK every ten minutes. I have had hundreds of beauty treatments and without a doubt the ones you feel best after are the ones you sleep through.

So maybe the key to staying young after all is as simple as sleep?

CHAPTER ELEVEN

The Botox Diary

Wednesday midday.

This is as close to cheating as I've ever come.

'You're not going to get any Botox done, are you?' Rupert said as I left the house this morning. He knows I am going to HB Health; he knows I am going to interview the lady who deals with all things related to needles there. He is already suspicious. I have not yet made the final leap from non-invasive to invasive treatments, as they are called in the trade, but if I'm honest I don't think I can resist temptation any longer.

'No, of course not,' I reasure him as I kiss him goodbye. I think I meant it at that moment, but the closer I get to Beauchamp Place the less sure I am.

It is a bright, cold winter's day. Nurse Brenda sits opposite me in a white leather chair. Next to us is a desk with a glass top; to the right of the desk is a couch covered in white paper. I can hear the endless stream of traffic outside.

'We have to decide whether this is the right treatment for you,' says Brenda. 'What disturbs you the most?'

'This.' I point at *the* wrinkle. 'This vast wrinkle in between my eyebrows. As well as my whole forehead, the line down the side of my face, the myriad of lines around my eyes, the lines just starting to form above my lips. In fact, my lips are horrible, far too small. Shall I go on?'

Brenda stares intently at my face. It's very bright in her office and I am almost embarrassed to have someone study my wrinkles so intently. It's rather like showing someone a big spot and then letting them get their magnifying glass out.

Brenda is a delicate lady, of Asian descent and totally wrinkle free. She could be aged anywhere between twenty-five and forty – I have no idea. But it's a look I am keen to emulate. Brenda came to England from the Philippines in 1993 and has been working in anti-ageing treatments ever since. She was one of the first nurses in the UK to practise Botox, so has been doing it for over eight years.

Botox. For a while the name seemed to me vaguely

threatening, something dangerous, rather like a soft drug that leads on to heroin and your eventual destruction. The medical description doesn't exactly fill you with a desire to inject it into your face. It is a vacuum-dried purified Botulinum Toxin produced from clostridium Botulinum. What it actually does is block transmission between the nerve endings and the muscle fibres, thus weakening the muscle and preventing it from moving and causing wrinkles. It was first developed in the 1960s to treat neurological disorders. It has been used cosmetically since 1987 when Dr Jean Carruthers in Vancouver discovered its potential. She used it on patients with misaligned eyes. One day a patient shouted at her for not injecting it in between her eyes. Dr Carruthers said she didn't think the patient needed it there. The patient told her she didn't but that every time she treated me there she got this beautiful, untroubled expression. Dr Carruthers says that's when something clicked. That was back in 1987. Here I am twenty years later. Surely if there was anything really bad about this we would know about it by now?

Of course there are risks. According to Newby Hands, health and beauty director at *Harper's Bazaar*, Botox 'can migrate' but it wears off in time and the effect can be lessened by another jab. So that's all right then.

Newby has been Botoxed for six years and swears by it. 'It is one of the best non-surgical anti-ageing treatments around,' she says.

Some say that Botox can make you look frozen but Brenda says that this is not the fault of the Botox, rather the person who has administered it. 'They have clearly put too much in; an experienced practitioner will know how to optimise the effect.'

I have done some research on the internet. According to a website calling itself Botox Information, the possible side effects are as follows:

Headache
Flu-like symptoms
Temporary eyelid droop
Nausea
Squint/double vision
Twitching of the eye
Facial pain
Redness at injection site
Muscle weakness (well, that's the whole point
  isn't it?)

So at worst I will be a vomiting, twitching, sneezing lunatic. But at least I'll be wrinkle free.

It is the most popular non-surgical cosmetic procedure performed in the world. It lasts between three to four months, after which you will be back to your old wrinkly self. To date there are no documented complications associated with using it, although common sense might argue that injecting yourself with poison is never a good idea.

I call my friend Anne in Rhode Island for further reassurance and medical advice. She is a paediatrician and has been aware of Botox as a treatment for muscular conditions for many years.

'To date there appears to be no reported damage or cumulative effects at all,' she says. 'The body seems to metabolise the substance without any problem.'

All over the world people are mad about Botox. In the US between 2000 and 2005, use of Botox increased by 338 per cent, resulting in over 4 million Botox treatments out of a total of 10 million cosmetic procedures. People don't have Tupperware parties any more, they have Botox parties. It won't be long before the Avon Lady is replaced by the Botox Lady. She'll ring your doorbell and when you open your door she'll wave a small syringe in the air and chant: 'Botox calling.' And that's exactly where the danger lies. A dentist friend of mine said he was offered (by his practice) a one-day

Botox course, after which they were going to let him lose on the world. Much as I like my friend, I don't trust anyone with one day's training to erase a lifetime of frowning and smiling. In fact I'm still not convinced I trust anyone to do that.

In the UK it is estimated that over 100,000 people a year have Botox. There have been reports in the press that Botox is addictive. It's not exactly something you inhale or smoke but obviously, if it works, people will come back for more. Wouldn't you? Here's something that removes your wrinkles, doesn't involve a scalpel and is not totally unaffordable. There's nothing addictive about it at all. People just don't like wrinkles.

Brenda takes notes as she stares at me. I dread to think what she's writing, but I suppose she's seen worse. After all, I am in the hands of the master here. I have seen Brenda's handiwork; she does the Botox and fillers for everyone at Heather Bird Health; and a very nice-looking bunch of people they are too. Vanessa, the nutritionist here, for example, has had her lips done. But you really can't tell. She just looks very pretty and totally normal, not even a hint of a trout-pout.

This is the thing about Botox. If you are going to

have it done, have it done by someone you know and trust, someone whose work you have seen.

I ask Brenda if she's ever had any bad results.

'I've had bad results because of too much expect-ation,' she says. 'Some people come in and say they don't want any movement at all, they don't want to smile, or be able to raise their eyebrows. But what happens then is that other areas start to compensate. A client of mine wanted no movement at all in her forehead but then her scalp started sinking downwards because it was compen-sating for the immobility in her forehead and eyebrows.'

'Who is the youngest person you have ever treated?'

'I treat Julie, who works here, with Botox and she is twenty-three, but it's more of a preventative measure for her. I think that's a good age to start. One girl came in asking to have her lips done and she was only seventeen. I refused; I didn't feel comfortable doing it. A lot of our work is to manage expectations. We have a responsibility to patients; we are not here to cheat them.'

No, but we are here to cheat the wrinkles.

'You have an animated face,' says Botox Brenda. 'I can see you smile a lot.' She pauses, then adds hastily, 'Which is good.'

She asks me to frown and then to smile.

'The lines you have could be treated with Botulinum Toxin,' she says. I feel my heart skip a beat, like a teenager hearing the name of her secret boyfriend. 'It will also act as a good prevention for further lines.'

'But they won't go away altogether?' I ask. I remember when a photographer took some pictures of me for my column in the *Sunday Times*. She asked me to smile and my wrinkles looked awful so she offered to delete them with the help of Photoshop. I looked like an android afterwards, totally unnatural.

'They will be a lot softer. Let me show you.' Botox Brenda puts a mirror in my hands and walks behind me. She places her hands on my forehead and pulls. 'This is with Botulinum Toxin,' she says. 'And this is without.' She lets go. Then she does the same on the area around my eyes. I can't actually believe anything will make that much difference short of a full face-lift. This is miraculous. I will look ten years younger. So even if Rupert does divorce me it should be easy enough to find another husband.

'With Botulinum Toxin you won't see it straight away,' she says. For some reason she is insisting on using its full name, maybe it's a legal thing. 'It will take about three or four days for you to see anything at all and up to two weeks for the full effect. With the fillers that we

217

use to plump up lips you will see a result immediately. You mentioned something about your lips?'

'I hate them, they're too thin. But I don't want a trout-pout.'

'I would probably just do a little on the contour of the upper lip and something for the body of the lower lip. Also the corners of your mouth go down a little and we need to lift that. Now fillers are more painful than the Botox and you will look like you've had a trout-pout for at least two days. The lips swell up a lot.'

Today is Wednesday, on Monday I go on television to promote my latest book. This is not a good time to look like I've been punched in the mouth.

Botox Brenda shows me how my lips would look. I don't like it. It doesn't look like me.

'What do you think I should do?' I ask her.

'I think you should do the upper face with Botox and the filler to lift the corners of your mouth. That way you keep the costs down as well.'

Ah, yes, the cost. All this staying young doesn't come cheap. If I'd known I would have avoided laughing all my life, now I can just be miserable paying for it. The fillers are £250 each and the Botox injections £198 each.

'But you know there is no point in just coming in and having a one-off treatment,' says Brenda. 'This is a work in progress and you have to maintain your Botox to get the best out of it.'

I suppose she would say that, wouldn't she?

I sit there thinking for a few minutes. The downside could be any of the side effects I mentioned earlier, along with a very grumpy husband. The upside will be an almost wrinkle-free me. Brenda is waiting for a decision. I definitely do not want to do the lips. But do I want to leave her office looking the same as I do now? Whatever else, it is good research for the book, I tell myself.

'Let's do the Botox and the fillers to lift the mouth, but not the lips,' I say to Brenda. I am a literary martyr.

Wednesday, 12.30 p.m. – on the couch.

'Have you signed the form?' asks Botox Brenda, preparing her syringe.

'Yes, I've signed my life away,' I reply.

'Don't think of it like that!' Brenda laughs.

I laugh too but I am a little nervous, beneath the excitement. My husband's words, 'You need braintox, not Botox,' are echoing around my head as I watch Brenda prepare for the treatment. If it all goes horribly wrong I'm in deep trouble. Not only will Rupert hate me and think I'm even more stupid than he does now, but I could end up with a rash all over my face or an involuntarily twitching eye. Really attractive.

Brenda starts stroking my forehead and I begin to relax. It occurs to me as I lie on the couch that Botox is probably cheaper than psychotherapy and possibly a lot more effective. For around £400 you can walk out knowing that in a matter of days you will be better-looking. I find that a hell of a lot more comforting (and useful) than knowing that my mother made me hate anchovies.

Brenda has taken a series of Polaroid pictures of me, so we can do a before and after. The idea is that I come back in a week's time so she can see if my Botox needs topping up and make sure everything is all right. For the pictures I had to smile and frown and raise my eyebrows. Consequently I look quite mad. Whatever happens on this couch today, it's not possible to look any worse than that.

'Frown for me,' says Brenda now, needle in hand. She pinches a piece of my skin. 'It's a tiny needle and only the tip goes in, so it shouldn't hurt too much. The fillers are much more uncomfortable.' Great, so that's something to look forward to.

'How was that?'

'Amazingly I hardly felt a thing.'

'Good. People have different pain thresholds; yours is obviously quite high. Now frown for me again.'

Botox Brenda dances around my face, pinching bits of skin and jabbing her needle in, then massaging the point she's just jabbed. Actually that's the most painful bit. After about ten minutes all the Botox is done.

'Now don't touch it, but you're to keep frowning, smiling and raising your eyebrows every few minutes for the next two hours. Don't lie flat for six hours and no strenuous exercise for six hours. Now for the fillers.'

Brenda injects the side of my face; it doesn't hurt at all.

'OK, take a look,' she says, handing me a mirror.

'I can see specks of blood,' I say, suddenly feeling quite weak.

'Compare it with the other side.'

I have to admit it is amazing. Now that Brenda has wiped away the blood, I can see that the whole left side of my face looks younger. It's lifted the entire area. It looks brilliant. I can see how this could become addictive. Suddenly I am a changed woman. This is a transformation and it's taken all of three seconds. Brenda has achieved something with her needle no amount of exercise, healthy food or vitamins could do. I almost can't believe it. Why isn't everyone doing this?

The other side is more painful, but not too bad. Suddenly I look happier, as well as younger.

'You can wear make-up in half an hour,' says Brenda, shaking my hand as I leave. 'But don't forget to keep frowning, smiling and raising your eyebrows.'

Wednesday, 4.30 p.m.

Am almost arrested for pulling strange faces at the Chanel counter in Harvey Nichols in an effort to keep frowning, smiling and raising my eyebrows. Luckily when I explain what I'm doing, the girl totally understands. She's been there, done that Botox thing. 'Forget the face creams,' she whispers conspiratorially. 'Botox is where it's at.'

Wednesday, 6 p.m.

I catch sight of myself in a mirror as I walk down the King's Road towards the Phoenix pub where I'm meeting my friend Rachel. I look like I'm smiling. My face looks happier, somehow more relaxed.

Wednesday, 6.30 p.m.

I smile inanely at Rachel.

'You're not pregnant again, are you?' she asks.

'*Noooo*. Can't you see a difference?'

'Is that a new jumper?'

Wednesday, 10 p.m.

Am taking my make-up off, no visible change to my forehead, but then Botox Brenda did say it would take two to three days. Go to bed very excited by the thought of what I might look like when I wake up. Assuming the Botox is working at double speed, that is. With the amount of frowning and smiling I've been doing it should be.

Thursday, 8 a.m.

All I have to show for yesterday are bruises where the fillers went in. I cover them with some make-up. I feel a little dowdy and quite sore. My forehead feels heavy.

Thursday midday.

I have a mild headache, which I take to be a good sign. No vomiting or twitching yet. But *the* wrinkle is still there. 'You're not long for this world, buster,' I keep telling it. It doesn't look worried.

Friday, 10 p.m.

Am jolly pleased with the way I look as I stumble to bed, having drunk half a bottle of champagne and three glasses of Pinot Grigio. Am staying in Sussex with my friend Annika. She is a former model and really too beautiful to be friends with, but too amusing not to. Maybe not the best person to be around when you're in the middle of a surgical procedure. I fall into bed praying the Botox will work by the morning.

Saturday, 8 a.m.

My forehead feels very heavy; in fact it feels like there's a slab of ice on it. But this could be the effect of the alcohol.

Saturday, 10 a.m.

This must be how people live when they don't have children. They wake up feeling dreadful and then they go back to sleep. I stumble into the bathroom and see for the first time that the Botox is really starting to kick in. My forehead is almost wrinkle free. Botox Brenda has triumphed. But rather worryingly a new wrinkle has appeared, right at the top of my forehead. This one is obviously compensating for the fact that the others have been ironed out. Hopefully it will vanish in time as well.

Saturday, midday.

I am spending most of the day in front of the mirror monitoring my forehead. It still feels very heavy. I wouldn't describe it as a headache but rather like someone is holding a metal plate against my forehead. It might feel odd but looks a lot better. I am wondering if this is as good as it gets. Is there any more effect of the Botox still to come? The crow's-feet are still there, as is *the* wrinkle, so I hope there is.

Sunday, 9 a.m.

EUREKA! *The* wrinkle has gone. Well, almost. It is a shadow of its former self. Ha! And the crow's-feet are slowly slipping away . . .

Monday, 8 a.m.

Am slightly amazed at how far back I have to lean to get my mascara on. My eyelids seem to have doubled in size. This is slightly disconcerting. I am no longer in control of my face and its contents.

Monday, 10 a.m.

Am in the *Five News* make-up room.

'Can you look up please?' asks the nice make-up artist.

'I'm afraid that won't be possible,' I reply.

Monday, midday.

I call husband to ask what he thought of my TV appearance.

'It didn't really seem like you,' he says.

I decide that a phone call from London is not the time to break the news about my betrayal.

Monday, 6 p.m.

Drinks with friends I am staying with and a rather glamorous Tory MP, who is always on TV.

'You look amazing,' he says when I walk in the room. 'France obviously agrees with you.'

I decide not to ruin his image of fresh air, good food and good living being responsible in any way whatsoever for my appearance.

Tuesday 8 a.m.

Eyelids looking worryingly saggy. That one wrinkle across the top of my forehead is still there as well. It looks terribly unnatural, just one long line, really not what you need.

Tuesday 10 p.m.

Smiling seems a little trickier than it used to be. The upside is that when I do manage to smile, the crow's-feet are really minimal, so when I smile I look younger, not older. All in all I am very pleased with the results.

❖   ❖   ❖

Wednesday, midday.

Exactly a week on, I decide to see Brenda about the new wrinkle. She says we'll get that one next time. She takes some photos for her records. My face looks a bit lopsided – is that a result of the Botox? She shows me the photos from before the treatment. My face was lopsided then as well. And more wrinkly.

Thursday, 8 a.m.

Am on my way home. I wonder if my husband will notice.

Thursday, 8 p.m.

Am home. He hasn't noticed a thing. Should I tell him? Probably best to wait until the morning. Maybe in the morning light he'll notice.

Friday, 8 a.m.

Looking at my face for the first time properly in the daylight in my own mirror at home I see that there is a huge difference. I really do have fewer wrinkles. It's amazing. I look around my bathroom at all the creams I have spent years using. Do they do anything at all? Certainly not in comparison with Brenda Botox and her magic needle.

The worrying thing now is that I can't see how I'll ever live without this. I quickly call Mary for advice while Rupert is watering the garden.

'Should I tell him?'

'What's the point?' she asks, but is more interested in the results of the Botox than my marriage. 'Does it really look better? I can't wait to see you. Can I come next time?'

My husband brings me a glass of orange juice.

'It's lovely to have you home,' he says, hugging me. I wait for him to add: 'And you look incredible, at least ten years younger, London obviously agrees with you.' Then I can confess. He doesn't, so I keep quiet. I feel like a traitor. A wrinkle-free traitor.

Two weeks later at a bar in Montpellier.

A romantic dinner out may seem an unlikely place to confess everything to my husband, but I get drunk. There is a slight misunderstanding on the number of Caipirihnas we order and I end up drinking two, which sends me over the edge.

'Have you noticed anything different about me?' I ask him, swaying gently.

'No, should I have?'

I tell him what I did in London on my last trip.

I am extremely nervous, but the alcohol is making me brave.

He almost falls off his chair, but that could be the effect of the Caipirihnas.

'You mean you just went ahead and did it?' he asks. 'Even when you said you wouldn't?'

'Yes, I know, I'm sorry, but she was there with her needle and I just thought it would be good for the book, and anyway it wears off.'

'That's just plain dishonest.'

'I know, I know.' I wonder if crying might be the best strategy here, but instead opt for total surrender. 'I'm so sorry but I knew you'd stop me and it was just one of the things I had to try. I mean, everyone is talking about it, it would have been ridiculous to write a book about ageing and not try Botox, for heaven's sake.'

'You're going to turn into one of those mad women we used to laugh at, aren't you?'

'No, of course not. I won't be having my lips done.'

'You say that now, but what's next? Surgery?'

'Never,' I say as solemnly as my alcohol levels will allow me to. 'No scalpels, I swear.'

'It is odd,' he carries on, 'but when I saw you on the Channel Five news I asked myself, "Who is this woman I'm married to?" It was a horrible feeling. I just didn't recognise you.'

'And now?'

'Now you seem to be back to yourself. But you're right,' he says, peering at my forehead, 'you do have fewer wrinkles. It's incredible.'

I smile. 'Look, no crow's-feet,' I crow.

'Actually,' he begins, 'I don't know if you've noticed, but I've had my willy enlarged.'

For a moment I look down at his crotch and then I realise I'm just drunk, not stupid. 'Very amusing. Anyway, do you like the new Botoxed me?'

'Yes, but the problem is I can't see when you're ever going to stop.'

'Oh, no,' I protest. 'This was just a one-off for the book.'

But I already know that I'm lying and that when I next see Botox Brenda, I'll jump back on her couch quicker than you can say, make mine a Caipirihna, or two. And why stop at Botox . . . ?

CHAPTER TWELVE

Ten Years Younger in Three Days

I've booked myself in for an anti-ageing weekend and it starts before I even get on the plane. I am at the Virgin Clubhouse in Heathrow where I am scheduled to have an anti-ageing eye mask and a St Tropez tan. Then it's off to New York for a selection of treatments that promise to transform me into a younger version of myself in just three short days. I firmly believe that the Americans are way ahead of us when it comes to anti-ageing and I need to go there to find out more.

I have done a lot of travelling for this book and of all the times I have left the children, this has been the worst.

'Don't be gone go,' said my little boy last night when I kissed him good night. By the time he woke up this morning I was 'gone go'. At the airport my phone rings.

'I want you,' says a little voice. It's enough to make me want to leap over the security barrier and fly back to Montpellier.

The girls were sad last night as well. I felt worse than the Wicked Witch of the West as I packed my bags, and more miserable (although I do wonder if witches are ever miserable? I mean normally they just get to do what they want).

Rupert gives me a picture he's cut out of a newspaper before I leave. It is a close-up of a Swedish actress clutching her dog. I remember her from when I was growing up. Then she was stunning: long hair and legs, and über-stylish sunglasses. Now, I am sad to say, she looks very different. Her whole face is stretched and strange. What few wrinkles there are on her face seem to be in the wrong place. Her lips are like a buoyancy aid. Her eyes are too prominent, almost Marty Feldman-like. The dog too has mad, staring eyes. In fact, rather uncannily, she looks like her dog.

'I don't want you coming back looking like our dog,' says Rupert, shoving the picture into my hand. 'That's all I'm going to say.'

Despite the angst of leaving my family, the Virgin Clubhouse is fun. There is an enormous amount of food and drinks to choose from. I can't even decide where to sit, let alone what to eat. There is a cocktail bar, there are sofas, there are groups of chairs in clusters around tables, there are two chairs suspended from the ceiling in front of a running water wall. They remind me of pods from which aliens might be born. In the end I opt for the brown leather sofa as it has a plug in the armrest and I can save my laptop battery for the flight. I drink a fruit smoothie, eat Eggs Benedict and then drink green tea followed by Jasmine Pearl tea. More tea than a normal person would drink in a day, let alone an hour, but I have to try it. It is strong and full of flavour, in fact almost too much flavour. A rather large American on the next sofa declines to have anything at all. How could you do that? From Martinis to champagne, from fruit drinks to wine – I mean, surely you'd have to try *something*?

There are lots of single men and women around, and I don't know if it's just me but I think there's an air of adventure. I guess they are all on business and what better place to arrange a mile-high experience than the Clubhouse? Sadly my Colin Firth lookalike is not here. At least that would have taken my mind off the children.

But even more impressive than the Colin Firth look-alike is the fact that the lounge has a spa. With a Jacuzzi. Can you imagine? From the Jacuzzi to the plane; how cool is that? Never mind the mile-high club, join the frothy-bubble club. The spa is called the Cowshed. There is also a hairdresser called Bumble and bumble. As one of the treatments I have booked in New York is with a genius hairdresser I am not going to do anything to what remains of a dreadful haircut I recently got (cost £235), which depresses me every time I look in a mirror. I had to cut it into a short bob in an effort to perk it up a bit. Fernando was away so don't blame him. My hair is too thin and straggly to support a bob so instead of bouncing around my face, Anna Wintour-like, it just hangs un-convincingly. It's almost enough to make me wear a baseball cap. Instead I opt for Collagen Eye Treatment, which promises to detoxify, reduce puffiness and combat fine lines. All in less than half an hour.

I am led into a cubicle by Sian, an attractive blonde girl who has worked for Virgin for just over a year. She used to do in-flight treatments but has handed in her wings and has been happily massaging and pampering customers for the last four months on the ground. The treatment starts with cleansing and exfoliating; the prod-ucts are all aromatherapy-based and smell lovely. Sian starts to massage my neck and shoulders. Then she works her way up to my eyes, seeking out pressure points. The collagen follows; it is cold and soothing, and I try to ignore the advice of my beauty guru, Tina Richards, who claims it won't really do me any good at all.

'There is absolutely no point at all in putting collagen on your face,' she says. 'Collagen bundles reside in your dermis, way below the dead skin cells on the surface of your skin where one applies creams. There is also no evidence that taking collagen supplements has any effect either.'

It may not be getting to my dermis but it is very relaxing. Sian puts an eye mask on me and massages my head. There are many worse ways to spend time at the airport.

Next is the St Tropez tan. Throughout my anti-ageing quest I have been on the lookout for a sensible alternative to sitting on a beach: could this be it? Sian leads me into another cabin with a white round cubicle. I am slightly reminded of a Mystic Tan experience I once had and my heart sinks. I can't bear to spend another ten days with strange-coloured nails, the only major result I got from the last spray tan I tried.

Sian asks me to put on a paper thong, a black one, which is unusual; normally these disposable thongs come in just one colour, medicinal white. I say that I would rather not, there's really no need for a bikini line when one's not wearing a bikini. But Sian makes it clear the thong is *de rigueur*. So off come the clothes and on goes the thong. I step onto some strange silver bits of cardboard shaped like feet. Sian rubs cream onto my toe-and fingernails, my hair gets wrapped in a towel and I am asked to step into the cubicle.

'What do I have to press?' I ask.

'Don't worry,' says Sian. 'I am going to hand-spray you. The results are much better.'

I am asked to stand in a series of positions while Sian points a small spray-gun at my body, which emits a fine mist.

'You'll see a result straight away,' she says. 'But the effects will keep getting better as the day goes on. Don't have a shower for at least four hours.'

After the spraying I am left in the cubicle to dry off. I take a peek underneath my thong. There is a white line. Just the words 'St Tropez tan' had my husband scoffing 'chav' at me as I left the house this morning, but I have to say so far I like it. The colour is subtle but deep and it doesn't smell too much of fake tan. By the time Sian comes back with a glass of chilled sparkling water I am as bronzed as I've ever been.

'The tan lasts about a week,' she tells me. 'Then you need to start exfoliating.' She wipes my nails with something resembling a baby-wipe and leaves me to get dressed.

When I come out, my flight is ready to board. It has been the most civilised way to prepare for a transatlantic flight I have ever experienced. The treatments at the Clubhouse are all free. Only problem is, you need to buy a premium economy or upper class ticket to get in there in the first place. Could be a tad on the expensive side for a week's tan. But then again probably cheaper than lying on a beach for a week, and certainly less ageing.

On the flight to New York I try to define what it is about ageing that scares us so. I have now spent several months running around the world, experiencing some of what there is to offer on the anti-ageing front. This is an industry that is worth billions of pounds a year. Some women probably spend more on anti-ageing treatments than several small African countries spend on their annual health budgets. In fact, for some women with nothing else to do, fighting age is a full-time job.

Why do we all fight it? Why are we so reluctant to just let it happen? Is it really so bad?

In the Jenny Joseph poem 'Warning' she talks with glee about welcoming old age and with it the right to wear purple with a mismatched red hat. Seems like a great attitude to me.

I remember my grandmother once cycling along the pavement and someone shouting at her as she almost ran them over.

'I'm so old I can do what I want,' she responded in feisty spirit. She might even have been wearing a red hat at the time. But somehow that's not enough. My grandmother eventually ended up in an old people's home and after several years there decided to go on hunger strike until she died.

The most obvious reason we hate the idea of ageing is that it brings us closer to death. As La Rochefoucauld said: 'One cannot look directly at either the sun or death.' My eighty-four-year-old father points out that old age is the only thing between us and death, but for the most part old age is rarely viewed as a positive thing.

My parents-in-law came for dinner recently. Leonardo was sitting on my mother-in-law's knee.

'You're old,' he said to her. My reaction was totally instinctive. I was horrified and started apologising and telling him that wasn't a very nice thing to say to Granny. But the fact is, she is old. She looks great, but she's over seventy, which makes her an old woman.

Consider the following: old cow, old trout, old bag, old hag. Not many terms of abuse have the word young in them. As Marcel Proust says in *Remembrance of Things*

Past: 'You have not, perhaps, any personal merit – I've no idea, so few people have! But for a time at least you have youth, and that is always an attraction.'

Youth is attractive; old age is not, at least in our society. Youth is sweet, old age is sour. As Aristotle said, 'Young people are in a permanent state of intoxication because youth is sweet and they are growing.' Is this why old people become bitter?

When I talked to my mother about ageing, she was brutally honest. She told me that you do get bitter; you get bitter because you no longer feel young and full of energy and you resent others that do. You also have no interest in sex at all and as a result begin to enjoy life less. And you also know things can only go downhill. So what is there to look forward to? Then you get even more bitter and grumpy, people hate you more and so it goes on. A vicious circle of ageing.

The first thing I do when I get to New York is look up an old boyfriend. There's something quite odd about seeing someone you last saw when you were both unmarried and childless. It's like you both belong to a different life now and have suddenly landed on the same planet again. It's also a good indicator of how well or how badly you've aged. You can compare wrinkles (obviously after my Botox I have the upper hand) and body-shapes. What's odd about ageing is that inside I haven't changed very much at all; years and years have gone by but still I don't feel that different from how I did when I first met Tim in a house in Notting Hill Gate.

Of course, I was in love with him before he even arrived. He was a Cambridge graduate, a Ralph Lauren model and a soon-to-be published author. What's not to like? The bad news was that he arrived with my friend Iona, who was also keen on him, although they weren't going out.

Tim and I had a very grown-up argument about the merits of *Eugene Onegin*, the opera versus the ballet. I was mad about the ballet and couldn't imagine the opera would be anything in comparison. The next day he bought me the tape (shows how long ago that was) and I fell in love. Mainly with the opera, but also with Tim.

So here I am, on a freezing morning in New York, on my way to Grand Central Station to meet the man who almost caused my one and only fall-out with Iona and introduced me to one of the best operas ever written. The last time I saw him was at his wedding in New York about eight years ago. I wonder how much he's changed and, more importantly, will he think I've aged or be incredibly impressed with the new Botoxed, wrinkle-free me?

We've arranged to meet at the information pagoda in the middle of the station. 'It's where everyone meets if they're having an affair,' says Tim.

I arrive early and walk in through the heavy glass and wooden door. It is the most beautiful building: marble floors, brass fittings, Beaux Arts architecture, vast arched windows and a hushed atmosphere despite the rush-hour crowds. The marble staircase I walk down is modelled on the one at the Paris Opera House. It reminds me of a cross between a library and a museum. It seems incredible that half a million people pass through it every day on their way to work or home, or to meet lovers by the information pagoda.

I walk to the pagoda and look at its four-faced clock. It's 9 a.m. on all four faces, the time we're supposed to meet. By five past he still isn't there. I wonder how many people have waited here for dates that never showed up.

'Hi,' says a familiar voice. He's looking very down-town New York, wearing a corduroy jacket and trousers, carrying a folder with bits of paper. He reminds me of a university professor. He doesn't look at all like he did when I first met him.

We hug.

'How are you?' I ask.

'Fine. Look at you, looking all French. What's with the silly hat?' He takes my incredibly trendy peaked cap off my head and puts it on. 'See? This is how stupid it looks.'

Tim has clearly not mellowed with the years.

We sit down for a coffee and I tell him the reason for my trip to America. Tim has a surprisingly draconian view on anti-ageing treatments, even worse than Rupert's.

'I told my wife that if she ever has anything done at all, then that's it.'

'Who the hell are you to tell her that?' I say indignantly, inwardly congratulating myself on not marrying this bully. 'That's up to her, isn't it?'

'No, I really disagree with it; I find it all totally offensive. I just had to write a letter to my son's school: they were having a lottery and one of the prizes was Botox injections. Can you believe it?'

'Can I believe it? Where can I get tickets? I love Botox.'

He looks at me. 'You've had Botox?'

'Yes,' I smile. 'What do you think?'

'I think you look like you've got some wrinkles missing,' he responds, looking at me more closely. 'It looks freaky.'

'Thanks,' I say, wondering if I should mention that

242

he himself did look a lot better last time I saw him and he actually had some hair left.

'What is this fear of ageing?' he goes on. 'What is wrong with letting nature take her course? I think ageing adds something to people's personalities and to their humanity. This whole anti-ageing thing is absurd. I know men who four years ago were as bald as I am and now they have full heads of hair. Have you any idea how weird that is?'

'Yeah, but I bet they look better,' I argue.

'Maybe. I just think going against nature is unnatural. I mean, take Demi Moore. I saw her last week when I was in LA for the Oscars. OK, she looks great but she's an android, a perfect creation and she goes around telling people how much each perfect part of her body has cost her. I can almost forgive it in an actress – she's already selling something that is unreal and unnatural – but not in a real person.'

'But instead of being traded in for a younger model, which happens to so many women when they age, she herself has done the trading,' I say. 'Your holier-than-thou attitude is all very well, but the fact is that men like you sit around saying they want their women unsullied and natural but then at the first opportunity run off with someone half their age.'

This has already happened to three women I know, and I'm not even that old yet. One fool even ran off with his secretary, who was all of twenty-four. 'Couldn't you think of something a little more original?' I wanted to ask him.

But what Tim says makes me think. Has this quest turned me into a superficial type who cares more about what she looks like than anything else? Am I obsessed with Botox and anything else I can get my hands on? No, I was always fairly superficial. I told you, people don't change. Having said that, I have always been aware of the benefits of living well, eating well and avoiding stress. But right now I want more superficial and immediate anti-ageing methods and New York is the place to get them.

After meeting Tim, I make my way to Madison Avenue. I take a picture of myself in front of the Chrysler Building, which I text to Carla. She lived in America for a few years and loves New York. Then it's off to work. I have a tight schedule, only three days in New York and so much anti-ageing to get in.

First stop is Rodolfo Valentin's hair salon at 1020 Madison Avenue. The entrance is not promising. It is all a bit louche. I could almost be in an Agent Provocateur shop. There are mirrors everywhere, chandeliers, wooden columns, women wandering around with a lot of hair, pink curtains, overly stuffed furniture and a lot of gold. It is a little like a scene from the film *Marie Antoinette*. There is a big sign in the wood-panelled lift that reads: 'Come in with the hair you've got, leave with the hair you want.' Now you're talking. Anything but this hair will do, I think, catching a glimpse of my sorry locks in one of the many mirrors.

I stand in the reception area. To my left is a winding staircase. At regular intervals there are heads with wigs on them. Curly, straight, red, blonde, brunette – every colour and style is catered for. A man walks down the staircase. He is exceptionally tall, has long dark hair, looks like he's spent at least half the morning in a St Tropez tanning booth and boasts the largest groin area I have ever seen outside a German porn movie (not that I've watched a lot of them). He approaches me, puts his hands on my shoulders and smiles broadly.

'But, my darling, I had no idea you were so *beautiful*,' he shrieks excitedly, throwing his arms around me. 'Hair infusions will be my welcome present to you. But first we do your roots. Mayer, come here, you need to do some colour on this English lady!'

I shrink a little in response to this rather informal greeting as Rodolfo Valentin waves his arms in the air and snaps his fingers.

A smaller version of the great man (also dressed in black but with a less impressive groin) comes running up to us. I am ushered to a chair in front of a computer with internet access. It's an amazing if weird experience, having my hair done while checking my emails. There is one from Carla.

'Lower Heyford,' it reads. 'Sunday. Drizzle. Dog bored; I'm bored. Sunday papers full of crap. But lo! What do I find on my phone (after 3,456 desultory games of Spider Solitaire)? A pin-up of my favourite author against what is clearly a cardboard cut-out picture from a mag of New York! Nice try, Helena . . . you think I don't know you're still in your office!'

Rodolfo comes to talk to me, my head now level with his groin. What kind of infusions are going on down there, I wonder. What happens at the top of the winding staircase he floated down? But I try to keep my eyes firmly on the mirror as Rodolfo tells me his life story. He is dressed all in black. His shirt is unbuttoned practically to his waist, his hips slim under his tight black trousers (oh, no, we're not back there again). He must be in his forties but he looks great. He tells me he is intrigued by my book.

'Age gracefully, bah,' he says in his husky Argentinean accent. 'I will do everything possible to be young. There is *no* limit. Never stop. No age gracefully, everyone should die in their high heels if possible. Age is an attitude. If you want to be old, you are old, if you want to be young, you can be. Women come here maybe forty, forty-five, "Why you cut your hair so short?" I ask. Well, I'm not so young any more, they say. Long hair is not ageing, it's the opposite. Women are scared of long hair. Rome is sexiest city in the world. She is old, but she has colours, character, style and magic, women are the same thing. The most beautiful picture looks better with a beautiful frame and the hair is that frame. I don't do hair; I do bodies. The first thing I examine is your neck, how tall you are, how short you are from neck to waistline. I do faces and I do bodies, everything is individual. Other salons are factories.'

He starts to play with my hair. 'For me you are too young for this,' he says. 'You have to have it long again. Today the bob is fashion, but you have no volume, look at this.' He flicks my almost non-existent locks around. 'This is no good. A girl with hair down to here is ten years younger. Why you need a stupid thing like Martha Stewart? But then I am not responsible if they sexually proposition you in the street. Is not my problem.'

He tells me he is going to transform my hair from

medium-length, mousy, thin hair to luscious, long hair. He will do this by attaching pieces of real hair to my existing hair that will blend miraculously with my own. He calls these hair extensions 'infusions' and they are his very own creation.

Rodolfo Valentin has yet to do anything but already I have the feeling he is a magician. His salon is buzzing and fun. There are women all over, laughing and shrieking as Rodolfo flirts with them outrageously. I overhear one conversation between a mother and daughter, both regular clients, Jewish, classically New York.

'She had surgery and was like, "Well, how do I look?"' says the mother.

'What did you tell her?' asks the daughter.

'What could I say?' replies the mother. 'She looks like a mad woman.'

Both shriek with laughter.

Rodolfo was born in Argentina. From the age of five he was good with his hands, making paper flowers. His mother wanted him to be a plastic surgeon. He quit medical school after nine months.

'It was too long for me to start creating,' he tells me. 'I didn't tell my mother anything, I went to find a job.' He saw an advertisement in a newspaper asking for a hairdresser. The owner of the salon had a television programme.

'I was eighteen, I was skinny, like a pole, full of energy and collagen, I didn't have any experience except what I'd been taught by an aunt in Buenos Aires, who did all her own hair and make-up. But I was very tall, very good-looking. The owner, she like my look, she say, "I don't know how much you can do for me, but you're hired." Six months later I was on TV, so I had to tell my mother I quit medical school. "You'd better have a job," she told me. "I don't want a lazy son." One year later I opened my own salon.'

Two years later he went to Paris to work on an international fashion show. There were two stages set up. One for him and another for a rival hairdresser.

'Who was there?' he says. 'Alexandre de Paris, the greatest of them all. Princess Grace hairdresser, Liz Taylor hairdresser, the Queen of England hairdresser. I looked myself in the mirror and say, you have to win. I put on my tightest white pants, my tightest white shirt, unbuttoned to here,' he says, motioning to his waist. 'I said, I have to do it, I want it so bad, I start to play. There was Alexandre's stage, my stage, they were all looking at him. He was the king. But then I show up, youth, good-looking, two metres with boots, slowly everybody turns, people there and there, they all come to my stage. Eventually he came down from his stage to my stage and say, "You work for me since now on." He hire me and we do shows in Europe and I learn so much for him.' Rodolfo stayed with Alexandre for two years and then he got a call from Argentina telling him his mother had cancer. As he tells me this his eyes fill with tears. It must have been years ago but he is still emotional about it.

'She was so beautiful,' says Rodolfo. 'And she said to me, "Every day my friend tells me I have cancer." What friend is this, I say, I want to kill her. "My mutilation is not my breasts," she tell me. "My mutilation is my hair. Every morning my friend the mirror says YOU HAVE CANCER." I did hair prosthesis for her with my hands. First it was rustic but later I perfected it.'

At this point my hair colour has been done and it's time for the 'infusions'. There are five people milling around me. In the middle of them is Rodolfo, ordering different colours, textures and lengths.

'My mother made me promise before she died that I would work for people who have chemotherapy because of breast cancer,' he says. 'I do. I am not a plastic surgeon, but I do plastic surgery with hair. And I help anyone I can. I love my poors, I am the Robin Hood. I work hard, I bought my small shop and house and start to work. Years later people discover me, because of my infusions. Now they call me the society hairstylist and my ego is vast. My salon in Long Island is 10,000 square feet. Everyone say, Rodolfo, it's beautiful, but why you need such a big salon? I need it because my ego grows so much it doesn't fit in this small salon!'

I cannot help but like this man, as much for his energy as for the miracles he seems to be performing. Rodolfo's hair infusions work a bit like a sandwich. Basically he has two pieces of (real) hair attached to a small adhesive strip about an inch long. These two bits act as the bread while your own hair is the prosciutto. 'Or the mozzarella, if you prefer,' says Rodolfo. 'But they don't damage the hair at all and they take an hour to put in, unlike normal "spaghetti" hair extensions.'

While I am at the salon I get chatting to the lady sitting in the chair next to me. She looks familiar, but as the only person I know in New York, apart from Tim, is called Sophie and is at home with her baby son, it is a mystery where I could possibly know her from. It turns out she is Dayle Haddon, the supermodel. I suppose I should say the former supermodel. She has been the face of Estée Lauder and of L'Oréal, now writes books and acts as a consultant for multinational cosmetics companies, specialising in products for women over forty. Her books are called *Ageless Beauty* and *The Five Principles of Ageless Living*. I can't believe my luck. I have run into one of the world's front-line experts on anti-ageing.

'What's your top anti-ageing tip?' I ask her.

Dayle turns to me. Her hair (like mine) is being dyed. It looks like a dark palm tree sticking out from the top of her head. All around her brow she has brown gunk. She may be perfectly dressed but all I can see is the large black gown Rodolfo has made her wear, which seems to be about three sizes too big for her. There are bits of cotton behind her ears to protect them from the hair dye, which make them stick out. I am looking just as glam.

'Always look your best,' she replies, smiling broadly.

Dayle's attitude is very different from a lot of women's (and from Rodolfo's). Her thesis is that beauty evolves with age and that we should embrace that beauty.

'Women should discover what is great about ageing instead of fighting it,' she says. 'Just fighting it is hopeless; we have to develop a new process. For example, I know Botox works for some people but it's not for me. Embrace your age, every age has gifts that it brings with it.'

Her five principles of ageless living are as follows: 'Stay connected', by which she means stay close to your friends and family; 'Honour your body', so do lots of exercise; Dayle loves yoga and also agrees Pilates is brilliant. 'The key is to keep moving the body,' she says. 'That way it will stay fluid.' The third principle is 'Nurture your spirit'. This refers to your attitude and also making time for yourself through, for example, meditation. Next is 'Discover your wisdom'. 'No way would I ever want to be twenty again,' she explains. 'All that insecurity and uncertainty. I am much happier now.' Finally, 'Look your best'. At all times, bar when you're at Rodolfo's with a head full of dark hair dye. 'And don't forget your sun protection and proper eating,' she adds. 'Use sunscreen every day, on the backs of your hands as well as your face. And if you have yellow teeth, get them whitened. There is nothing more ageing than yellow teeth. I don't care how perfect the face is, if the teeth are yellow the whole effect is ruined.'

'I couldn't agree more,' I say, smiling with my mouth shut. I have yet to have my teeth whitened.

'Another thing is just standing up straight and smiling,' she adds. 'This alone can take ten years off you.' Assuming you don't have yellow teeth.

Dayle must be approaching fifty now, I guess. She looks great. She is definitely a natural beauty. I can see no signs of Botox or fillers. She is extremely slim, petite and elegant. Her skin is perfect. I ask her what creams she uses.

'I like the L'Oréal Age Perfect range,' she says. 'And I think Neutrogena does some really good creams.'

'What about all the really expensive ones? Like La Prairie?'

'You're just as well off with Nivea,' she says. 'But whatever you use you must always moisturise. Moisturiser acts as protection between you and the environment.'

I am dragged off to have my hair dye washed out. After that Manuel dries it and preparations begin for the famous infusions. A table of long hair with a slight wave in it appears next to me. The hair is in several different shades; each clump is fixed to a thin see-through strip that looks like Sellotape. The great man arrives, shirt if possible even more undone, and starts to boss everyone about in Spanish. Then he begins to comb my hair, to look at it, to pull it close to my face, away from my face, to brush it back and see how it falls.

Finally the transformation begins. Rodolfo is working with three colleagues whose job it is to select the particular hair he calls for (as far as I can make out it's a question of colour), put some of the glue onto the thin strip that holds it together and then pass it to him. The master then presses the sandwich together over my real hair as close to my scalp as possible. He begins at the bottom of the back of my head. After about five minutes he casually flicks a few long locks over my shoulder. I yelp with excitement. This is going to be amazing.

Rodolfo works quickly. I can feel the back of my head filling with hair. Then he moves on to the sides. My hair is rapidly changing from short, thin and straight to long, thick and curly. With every infusion I look better.

'*Voilà!*' says Rodolfo, beaming at me in the mirror. The man is a genius. He is beyond genius. He is like a genie in a bottle. He has given me what I have wanted since I was about seven years old: thick, luscious locks. There is a slight curl in them that makes me look like a film star. They look incredible. I look incredible. How is it possible to walk into a salon feeling like a hedgehog on a bad hair day and leave two hours later looking like Eva Longoria? These actually seem to be part of me right from the beginning. They feel secure, they feel like they belong, and they don't feel like they're pulling my hair out, which is how I always imagined hair extensions would feel. They are beautiful. I have long, gorgeous, thick, shiny hair. I can't stop gazing at it. I feel like I've walked straight out of a L'Oréal advertisement. I remember asking a hairdresser in Rome what women want when they walk into a salon. He said simply, 'To be transformed.' Well, I am certainly transformed.

This much pleasure must come with a downside.

'Will they damage my hair?' I ask.

'Your hair is protected by the infusions on either side of it,' says Rodolfo. 'It will be in even better condition when you take them out than if you hadn't had them.'

'When I take them out?' I repeat in horror. I hadn't thought of that.

'You have to take them out after two to three months.'

'Can anyone in London do it?'

'No,' says Rodolfo. 'This is my system. You just have to come back to New York.'

This could be the most expensive hair-habit I have ever acquired. Rodolfo is kindly donating the hair and his services but the normal cost is over $1,000.

'Can I get them put back in?' With normal extensions you have to have three months off. I am already worried about three minutes without mine.

'Yes, the same day, no worries. You have a godfather now,' he says, hugging me.

I almost miss getting out of the lift I'm so busy gazing at myself as I leave for my next appointment. It is with Dr Theodorou. He is an uptown dentist who is going to whiten my teeth. I tried to have them whitened before in London; it cost me £600 and when they showed me the before and after pictures I was confused as to which was which. So my hopes are not high as I walk into his office between Madison and Fifth Avenues.

Dr Theodorou is your perfect preppy American: he is cute – there is no other word for it – with floppy dark hair and a perfect smile. But he also has bad news.

'If we go through with this, Miss Frith Powell, you are not allowed to eat or drink anything that isn't white for forty-eight hours.'

I suddenly remember this from last time.

'So no red wine?' I ask, hoping he'll say 'only Burgundy'.

'No.'

'But I can have white wine, can't I?'

'No.'

'How about a gin and tonic with some lemon?'

'Leave out the lemon.'

'A cheese sandwich?'

'Only if it is white cheese and you cut the crusts off,' he says, smiling his perfect smile.

I decide to go through with the treatment, despite the enforced detox. The treatment entails me putting on a rubber contraption that clamps my mouth open and makes me look like Hannibal Lecter. It's not the most comfortable thing I've ever worn, nor the most flattering. Dr Preppy rubs a gel into my teeth and goes to work.

The procedure is not at all painful; it's just a bit tedious, but Dr Preppy's leggy blonde assistant puts on a DVD for me, so I watch *Lost in Translation* while years of eating and drinking colourfully is wiped from my teeth. Every twenty minutes Dr Preppy comes back in and wipes something on my teeth.

'You should also floss regularly,' he says, explaining that it is very good for your teeth but can also add years to your life expectancy. Apparently the bacteria you remove can, if left, lead to heart disease and strokes.

After almost an hour I have never been so relieved to get anything off as I have that mouth-torture instrument. Now we'll see if it's all been worth it. My teeth were a D3, which was pretty far down on the chart. They are now an A1, which is second from the top. Expectantly, I bare my teeth, turn my head this way and that, hoping to be blinded by my flashing white smile. I might even get a job at the Clinique La Prairie. I gaze at my new smile. It looks great. What a huge difference. I look both healthier and younger. I'm amazed everyone isn't doing this. It has to be one of the safest, cheapest and most effective anti-ageing methods there is.

I leave Dr Preppy's office and flash my perfect smile at everything in sight as I head to Bloomingdale's before my next appointment. This one is making me slightly nervous. It's as close to surgery as I will go in my entire anti-ageing quest.

CHAPTER THIRTEEN

Still Getting Younger in New York

I am at a restaurant called Cipriani in downtown New York. The ceiling is high, the tablecloths yellow linen, the floor is stone and the walls are white. On top of the highly polished wooden bar stands a vast cast-iron pot with spindly twigs coming out of it. On the wall behind the bar is a large painting of a cobra, menacingly lifting its head against a background of bright foliage. From the middle of the ceiling hangs a large chandelier. Other pictures include over-sized Peter Beard prints and a rather strange painting of a girl walking naked past a crowd of on-lookers. The painting is not strange because the girl is naked, but because she looks somehow wrong. She is extremely thin, has almost no bottom, but vast tits. It would be physically impossible to be that shape. But as I look around me I realise that most of Cipriani's clientele look fairly similar.

To my right sits a woman wearing a giraffe-print silk shirt and tight black trousers. She is with a good-looking black man, whom she spends most of the meal trying to devour. This in itself is not a great thing to watch; in a restaurant I prefer to see people eating their food as opposed to their dates, but the way this woman looks makes it even more creepy. She is of Asian origin, with thick dark long hair. Her face has obviously had some work on it. Her eyes look unnaturally elongated and I wonder briefly whether she is able to close them at all. Her skin is taut, tanned and wrinkle free, but it is her mouth that disturbs me most. Her lips look swollen, uncomfortable, unnatural, like she's been stung by a posse of bees. She is obviously very proud of them as she pouts unnaturally at her date and snuggles up to him endlessly.

To my left is a table of two men and one woman, all aged around thirty. At first glance the woman is ferociously pretty, almost take-your-breath-away stunning. She is tall, slim; her long, slick brown hair is tied into a neat ponytail with a black scrunchie. Her features are fine, her complexion flawless, her nose petite, her brown eyes wide and clear. But when I examine her more closely the first thing I notice is that her breasts are about four sizes too big for her frame. Underneath that oh-so-subtle pink cashmere jumper lurk two implants from hell. Then

I look again at that face. It is perfect, but that's just it, it's totally flawless, almost too much so. There's no character there. It looks like it's been ironed.

The men she is with aren't much more natural: One of them, inexplicably wearing a cloth cap and clothes that make him look like the chimney sweep in *Mary Poppins*, looks as if he's painted on his five o'clock shadow with burned cork. Maybe he has just been performing in *Mary Poppins* and has come to Cipriani for his dinner, but I doubt it; he looks more like a management consultant than a musical star. The other man has strange curly hair that hangs around his unshaven face (but at least he really does have a five o'clock shadow).

To the other side of them is my personal favourite. She is a woman wearing a silver ski jacket and large dark shades. Granted, the lighting in Cipriani could be a little more subtle, but it is 10 p.m. and pitch-dark outside. From what I can see of her face it looks lifted, but really the only clue to her age bracket is her husband, who looks around seventy. I guess that's going to be the problem for all these women who spend most of their time in the cosmetic surgeon's clinic: eventually they'll just have to tell people their husbands are their fathers.

Opposite me is a preppy-looking couple. He is in chinos and a blazer; she is wearing a rather extravagant frilly black shirt of the kind I last saw when Duran Duran were in their heyday. Underneath the frills lurk yet another pair of Pamela Anderson-style boobs and when she smiles I see that her teeth are as white as the wall behind her.

It is not just the clientele of Cipriani that looks surgic-ally enhanced. The coat-girl has an extremely impressive bottom. This is JLo on steroids. I can't stop staring at it. Is it real? Is it implants? Has she been to Brazil for a Brazilian Booty operation? Or is it just those knickers you can buy that promise to give you the JLo effect? I search for a VPL on her sleek black trousers; there isn't one. Her face is pretty, although I think her lips have had some work.

Cipriani reminds me a little of that bar in the first *Star Wars* film, the one Luke Skywalker and Han Solo go into to secure a spaceship. Only instead of the punters being monsters, the people here are all beautiful, or trying hard to be. There isn't a duff one among them except a table of rather fat, old lawyers braying loudly, who turn out to be from England.

I notice that all the diners apart from me and the fat lawyers have been presented with the signature drink, a mixture of peach juice and champagne called a Bellini. Maybe you have to have had obvious plastic surgery to qualify.

But what I know, and the waiters at Cipriani don't, is that underneath my own oh-so-subtle pink cashmere jumper (a nicer shade than Little Miss Ski-Jump-Nose's actually) lurks a heavy black corset, a contraption that is helping to heal my latest procedure, performed by New York's most famous cosmetic surgeon and my new best friend, Dr Steven Victor, or Dr LookGood, as he's otherwise known.

When I walked in here I felt pretty good, mulling over what fab results might be lurking under my corset. But now as I look around at the assorted freaks I'm wondering if I have finally gone mad. Have I embarked on a journey that has no limits? If I carry on will I end up with a trout-pout, stretched skin and no husband? Do I really want to end up like the people I see around me? Or like that Swedish actress? Or even worse: like my dog?

Dr Victor has been described as 'New York's most famous cosmetic dermatologist' and Fergie's 'plastic fantastic'. The latter is, of course, not necessarily a recommendation but the fact that the rich and famous choose him to deal with their ageing issues makes him a good person to see during my quest.

He is based on Madison Avenue, where else? Earlier

that day I walked into a classic New York apartment block with a doorman who doesn't open the door but says good morning very politely. The lift is wood-panelled. It opens on the reception area where two girls sit fielding calls from desperate women. It is not an overly posh office, which I always think is encouraging; you don't want to feel they're making too much profit from you. On the wall there are cartoon-like line drawings of Diana Ross and Barbra Streisand. I wonder if they are clients. There is pop music playing in the background. In the hall I catch a glimpse of the thinnest woman I have ever seen before she vanishes – off, I'm hoping, to go and eat something.

After a minute or so Lauren, my soon-to-be new best friend's assistant, appears. She is a very pretty brunette, buxom, natural-looking and very smiley. She looks about nineteen but I learn later that she's twenty-six. She leads me down a corridor to meet Dr LookGood. I had expected him to have one of those vast offices with a clear glass desk and leather loungers; spartanly furnished and decorated in muted tones of beige. I imagined him wafting out from behind his immaculate desk wearing a white coat and greeting me with a perfectly false smile.

I got the white coat right, but the rest couldn't be less true. New York's top dermatologist shares his tiny, chaotic, cramped office with his assistant. The walls are covered with all sorts of things, from pictures of the staff's (adorable) children to posters advertising his products to a mini-surgical board detailing the day's procedures. Lauren's desk is along one side of the room, her computer perched at the end of it. Dr LookGood has his desk, which is totally cluttered with bits of paper, in the middle of the room next to a large window overlooking Madison Avenue. Behind him are bookshelves and in front of his desk are two chairs filled with people's coats and more paper. He stands up and greets me warmly. As he does so I notice a small embroidered cushion on his chair that reads: 'It ain't easy being king.'

He is a handsome man, tall and well built, with thick silver hair. His face is open and his skin good, which I suppose is an occupational hazard, or maybe a must.

'Welcome,' he says. 'How can I help you?'

'I'm here to find out how to stay young-looking,' I tell him.

'Stay out of the sun, don't smoke, keep a constant weight, exercise, eat a good diet, don't drink – all the good things that nobody does.' He smiles. 'We all say we'll do those things but we don't. We're talking about unrealistic aims so what you really should do is just come see your cosmetic dermatologist, then you can commit all the sins in the world.'

His answer reminds me of a line from *The Picture of Dorian Gray*. Lord Henry says: 'To get back my youth I would do anything in the world, except take exercise, get up early, or be respectable.' Staying young-looking doesn't only require a financial commitment but also a commitment to live a certain lifestyle.

I don't believe you can live any way you like and then just get yourself patched up. I think a sane mixture of the two must be the way forward, but that the emphasis surely has to be on the way you treat yourself every day. And yet, if I could cheat, wouldn't I? If not, what am I doing here?

The phones are constantly ringing; people wander in and out of his office. The atmosphere is chaotic but happy. Dr LookGood has over 100,000 clients on his books. What do they want?

'It's all about competition,' he says. 'They turn around and look at a young woman in the room. You don't get dressed up to go find another man, you don't get dressed up for your husband. You do it to impress other women, to be the prettiest. With men it's more linked to success. They see younger guys coming up the ranks and don't want to be replaced.'

'Do some people come in with unrealistic expectations?'

'They are looking for a dream come true but often we can deliver it. We stop the clock, we turn it back. With injectables we don't have to do anything drastic, a bit of Botox, a bit of SmartLipo, peels, a bit of this and that and you can make someone look really good. But you don't want to make a fifty-year-old woman look twenty, that's just silly. You want to make a fifty-year-old look great for fifty.'

'Do you think by the time my children are thirty, ageing will be a thing of the past?'

'Probably. We're working on a project right now whereby we're harvesting your stem cells and injecting them back into your skin and rejuvenating the skin totally. Already you can take stem cells and regenerate them into your heart muscle to rebuild the muscle.'

'Is there anything I can do about crinkly skin?' I ask. 'Like the décolletage and on my legs?'

'We can treat that with a laser called the Affirm Laser.'

'How young should you start all this stuff? I mean, Lauren is only twenty-six – she tells me she has already had her lips done. Will she ever stop?'

'Yeah, when she dies,' laughs Dr LookGood.

Lauren agrees. 'This can be about prevention as much as anything else,' she says.

'But seriously, there is a cut-off point,' he says. 'The worst thing women do is come in here with other women because they always tell them to do more. I have never seen a girlfriend sit in that chair and say no, stop, your lips are big enough. They always say make 'em bigger and I want to say no, as a guy we don't want women to look like that. The duck-lips-and-frozen-face look is not attractive. There is no charisma there, no sex appeal. All puffed up, all lipped up, can't move and can't talk, I just don't find that sexy at all.'

'Have you had many disaster stories?'

'I have seen so much bad work in England,' he says. 'We see really bad Botox, bad fillers, lips done with Restylane, which is a waste of time as it goes away every three months. You should use silicone but go to someone who is good. I do between three and five lips a day and I always under-inject. That way the client can come back for more if she wants more of an effect. It takes a few days to settle so I send them away to assess the first treatment, then they can have a top-up if they feel it's not enough. Basically everyone in the world has the same tools – there isn't a magic tool out there. The rest of it is education, experience and then artistic judgement. It's like a painter: give him the paints, an easel, a canvas, a set of instructions. It's the experience that makes Rembrandt and Picasso so good. It's that X factor. It's 20 per cent technology and 80 per cent skill.'

'What could you do about this?' I ask, grabbing my tummy.

'Oh, I could make that go away in an hour with SmartLipo,' he says. 'You're my perfect lady, little bit of fat after three babies.'

Now he's really got my interest.

'I would suck the fat out and then the laser heats your skin so it gets tighter.'

'How does that work?

'If you throw a piece of bacon on a griddle it shrinks. SmartLipo works along the same principle.'

It reminds me of Dr Ney's Thermage machine, which tightens your skin by making it believe it is being burned so the fibroblasts scurry round to protect it. I ask him if it's the same principle.

'Thermage is not efficient, and it hurts,' he says. 'You cannot heat the lower dermis effectively through the skin. In the US it's not popular any more. I would rather do SmartLipo. Lauren's had it done. I took away her bra-strap fat.'

He shows me before and after pictures. It seems that

most of his staff have had this miracle treatment, which is basically a much less invasive form of liposuction. There are several differences. First, you get to stay awake to watch the fat leave your body, meaning you don't risk death under anaesthetic. Second, the cannula used is much smaller, between one and two millimetres, so the healing process is much faster. Third (and possibly most importantly) the laser used to melt the fat is then turned on your skin, making your skin think it is being burned and causing it to tighten by encouraging your fibroblasts (a type of cell) to produce more collagen, which makes your skin tighter and thicker; in other words, younger.

A colleague of Dr LookGood's, Dr McShane, joins us. He has just performed a mini face-lift on a seventy-three-year-old woman. This is a face-lift you can have in your lunch break. The incisions are minimal and the patient is awake throughout. Imagine the scenario. 'Hello dear, what did you have for lunch today?' 'Oh, just a cheese and pickle sandwich and a face-lift.'

'This is Helena, a writer from England,' says Dr LookGood. 'She's writing a book about a personal journey into ageing.'

'It must be a very short one so far,' says Dr McShane, looking into my eyes and taking my hand. 'She only looks about twenty-four.'

Dr LookGood laughs. 'You can see why he's had so many children. He now wants to get married again and have three more children. You interested?'

'If I get my stomach done I'm not having any more children,' I say.

'But you could get pregnant again, no problem,' says Dr LookGood. 'The body has an infinite capacity to expand. Have you ever seen a fat person explode? You can literally do SmartLipo and gain weight or get pregnant – this will last for twenty years. Unless, of course, you gain like twenty-five pounds. Then I can't help you.'

It sounds great, too good to be true. I ask if I can see the mini-face-lift lady.

Arlene, as she is called, is lying on a bed covered in white bandages. She is thin and sprightly. Even though her head is bandaged, she looks extremely jolly.

'How was it?' I ask.

'It's wonderful, an instant face-lift,' she says. 'I can see there's a lift even though I'm recovering. The neck is amazing, you gotta see the neck.' She moves her towelling robe so I can see her neck. Looks good to me.

'What made you decide to do this?'

'The fact that you don't need to be put to sleep, that you can talk to docs and they're here watching you. I come here for dermatological problems. I had laser done, and a face peel a few weeks ago and my reaction has been so marvellous. Actually with the peel the recovery was longer. I had to stay at home for a few days while my skin peeled off.'

'How long is your recovery period with this treatment?'

'I'm going to a party tomorrow night,' she says. 'I'll wear a scarf but I'll be fine. It was an hour and half from start to finish and I was awake all the time. I'll leave in a minute and I'll walk home; I only live about five blocks away.'

Angela, the nurse, tells me that regular plastic surgery goes much deeper. You're asleep for an hour to two hours and it takes a week to get over. With this procedure you need to sit up for a few days and not do too much chewing but other than that there's not a lot of aftercare.

'Did you do this for the party?' I ask Arlene. 'Do you always make this much effort?'

'For a woman my age to get a procedure like this done lifts years away,' she says. 'You still *feel* so young. I read about people going into assisted care at seventy-five. Assisted care at seventy-five? That's for ninety-five-year-olds. I just took enforced retirement; I taught in a school all my life and then owned a restaurant for twenty years. And I'm not ready to give up just yet.'

For those of you who are not willing to go under the knife (me included) or even the needle (I'm thinking about it) there are a couple of alternatives. I can't tell you if they work, I'm afraid, because they both involve at least weekly sessions over a long period of time. One is the acupuncture face-lift.

The idea is that the two life forces known as the Yin and the Yang must be balanced to produce the life force known as Chi. Chi energy flows though the body along fourteen different pathways and the theory is that wrinkles and ageing is caused by out-of-synch Chi in various parts of the body. The problem with the acupuncture face-lift is that it is expensive and you also need a treatment a week for several months.

The other is the yoga face-lift (I kid you not). This is most popular in the US (no surprise there) and involves yoga exercises to reduce sagging and wrinkles, similar to Carolyn's facial exercising. There are even books about it, like *The Yoga Face* by Annelise Hagen. She teaches Revita-Yoga, which combines yoga and facial exercises. I would in general agree that yoga seems very anti-ageing – yogis always look at least ten years younger than they are – but am sceptical as to what it can do specifically for a wrinkle. Still, if it gets people doing yoga I'm all for it. No harm ever came from a few downward dogs.

So at 9 a.m. the next morning I find myself lying where Arlene was, ready to be SmartLipoed. How the hell did I get here? Yesterday, when Dr LookGood was talking about removing my stomach fat with a new easy technique it all seemed so easy, so breezy, but now it feels actually quite serious.

I haven't told my husband about this and I don't want to think about it. I know how he feels about cosmetic procedures. What I have told him is that I am doing something as part of research for the book and I promise that it doesn't involve general anaesthetic or scalpels.

'Good,' he said. 'I don't want you dying on me. You can't leave me with all these children.' Assuming I survive, I will have to explain my new midriff after the event and hope he forgives me. Or that he is so impressed with my flat stomach he decides to cross over to the other side and get his done as well.

But now, as I lie there on the operating bed the next day, wearing green surgical knickers and a paper shower cap (not a good look), and Angela the nurse works around me preparing me for the procedure, I suddenly have a panic attack. My tummy is covered in purple pen-marks

HELENA FRITH POWELL

where Dr LookGood is going to remove the fat. This is
as close to an operation (bar my caesarean) as I have
ever been and I don't actually have to do it. Am I going
to die? Am I going to leave my three children mother-
less for the sake of my potbelly? Have I gone mad? When
he was explaining it, I didn't even realise I needed to
wear surgical kit, or have my tummy covered in disinfectant, or even lie down. The way he described it was
as if I could walk in and have my tummy-fat removed
without even noticing it.

How did I make this slightly impulsive decision to go
under the laser? I suppose I convinced myself that it was
all in the name of research, and it was, in part. But there's
no denying that my main motivation is to get rid of my
tummy. I see Dr LookGood as a kind of magician who
will remove something I really don't need, and hate with
a vengeance. Something I have tried in vain to get rid of
for most of my life. Something that has made sit-ups an
essential part of my life, however much I hate them.

Before I have time to rethink, Dr LookGood arrives,
full of confidence. I have some local anaesthetic where
the laser goes in (just above my hips on either side) and
Dr LookGood injects a watery solution with painkillers
so that the part about to be treated doesn't hurt. I am
offered some Valium but decline. Dr LookGood and his

colleagues seem surprised but he gets to work with the laser about ten minutes after the liquid has gone in. Slowly, he manipulates it around my stomach. How can I describe it? It's not an unpleasant experience. As he moves the laser across my stomach, it doesn't feel like my own stomach, as if I am somehow detached from it. I remember when I had my caesarean I could feel the doctor's hands on me but felt no pain; this is the same. I can feel the laser moving inside my tummy and sometimes there's a bit of resistance but mostly it's just smooth and rather strange. I was expecting to smell something vaguely like scorched bacon. Thankfully, there is no smell at all.

As Dr LookGood smoothes the laser across my body he takes me through the operation. At one stage he turns out the overhead lights and all we can see is the small muted red beam of the laser beavering away in my tummy. It's all rather peaceful and I almost doze off in the darkness. The SmartLipo machine works for a total of just over thirteen minutes, hopefully making my fat deposits a thing of the past and firing my fibroblasts into action. Then Dr LookGood eases the cannula into the same hole the SmartLipo laser went into and I watch as my fat (it looks just like melted butter) is sucked up a tube and into a plastic container. This part isn't strictly necessary as the fat would just come out when you sweat or pee of its own accord but this way I'll get quicker results. In comparison to traditional liposuction, the recovery period is much shorter with SmartLipo. You should rest the first day, wear the corset for a week and take no strenuous exercise for two weeks. Angela the nurse told me to go and lie down after the procedure but on my way to the hotel I got distracted by Saks on Fifth Avenue for about four hours. What's a girl to do?

When I get back to the hotel just after lunch I am tired, very cold and shaky – totally my own fault for not following the nurse's orders. But at no stage does my tummy feel uncomfortable. It is protected by a rather pervy black corset that ends just below my breast, which helps reduce swelling and makes recovery quicker.

With traditional liposuction, the patient needs to stay in bed for up to seven days and wear a corset for six weeks. The total recovery period is more like eight weeks. You also have to have your stitches out. The tiny scabs I have where the cannula went should drop off within a few days.

Rupert calls that afternoon.

'So, can you tell me what you had done?' he asks.

'SmartLipo,' I tell him, and explain the procedure.

'Doesn't sound that smart to me,' he responds. 'But it's better than doing sit-ups. And at least it wasn't your lips.'

'No, my lips are as thin as they always were,' I re-assure him. 'Is that what you thought I was going to do?'

'Yes,' he says. 'I was worried you'd finally lost the plot. You haven't, have you? This is all going to end some day soon?'

'Of course,' I say. 'It's just for the book.'

But I'm not really telling the truth. It isn't just for the book any more. It's for me as well. I am intrigued to see how far I can go, to see how much of a difference I can make to myself with all this. Now that I'm away from the constraints of home, this adventure is just hotting up.

I sleep well and am ready for more anti-ageing action the following morning. I thought the corset would be uncomfortable during the night, but I barely notice it is there. I take it off rather gingerly before I get in the shower. I don't really know what I expect to find. Luckily nothing too drastic. The scabs where the cannula went in are still there, my stomach looks flatter, and my caesarean scar seems a little less pronounced. I am not in pain, getting dressed is easy, and my jeans seem a little looser. So far, so good.

My next anti-ageing appointment is with Dr Eric S. Berger, otherwise known as The Skin Doctor. He too has a very pretty, voluptuous, young receptionist. I wonder if his clients come in and say: 'I want to look like her.'

There is a bowl of apples on the desk in front of her. 'An apple a day keeps the wrinkles away,' reads a card.

'Is that really true?' I ask her, wondering how many you need to eat a day to look like her.

'We like to think so,' she says.

The Skin Doctor doesn't keep me waiting long. I have just about finished filling in the endless forms they hand you whenever you walk into a doctor's office in America, when he appears. He is tall and well built. I would guess he's in his late forties. We walk into his small and cluttered office. There are lots of framed medical qualifications on the wall behind his large wooden desk.

I tell Dr Berger a bit about the book I am writing.

'I think of ageing as a disease, not a process,' he says. 'It's a disease you can fight and how you fight it will determine how well or badly you age.'

'So what are the major factors?'

'One major factor is dead cell accumulation.'

'What is that? It sounds disgusting.'

'As children, our skin cell turnover is every ten days,' he explains. 'As adults, it's every forty-five days. So unless you cleanse every day and exfoliate at least once a month there is going to be stuff stuck in your pores which stays there and creates free radicals.'

Dr Berger looks in good shape. He tells me that his

father is ninety-four and still pumps iron three days a week. I am guessing he does the same. Everyone I have met so far does, especially Americans. It's a funny thing about American men; they seem to take much better care of their bodies than British men do. I went to the cinema with an American friend once to see a film with Hugh Grant in it. When he took his top off she hid under her cardigan. 'Ugh,' she said. 'He's so British.'

'What about procedures?' I ask Dr Berger. 'Which do you think are the best?'

'Lasers are the future of anti-ageing medicine. In twenty years' time, taking a knife to someone's face will be the equivalent of listening to their heart with your ear today,' he says. 'The Titan laser can take years off a face if you have three treatments spaced out at every four weeks. Whoever you see, make sure the doctor has a variety of lasers used to treat specific things. One doesn't do it all. I have seen horrendous complications as a result. If all you have is a hammer everything becomes a nail. Come with me, I'll show you.'

We walk into his treatment room. There is a couch covered in white paper in the middle of the room. Along one wall there is a sink and dotted all around are various machines.

'Meet my workhorse,' he says, introducing me to

his latest laser machine, the Cutera Xeo. This robot-looking contraption does everything from tightening the skin using the Titan head to removing unwanted hair. He switches the machine on and it rather terrifyingly begins to speak. Then, as he moves the laser over my hand, it peeps and finally performs something between a song and a sigh as it shuts down. He tells me it activates collagen production and the fibroblasts. The sensation of the laser is not unpleasant; it is warm, but I do smell burned hair. I look at the back of my hand for any sign of immediate rejuvenation; there is none.

'This can also take away sun spots and improve the texture and tone of the skin,' he says, 'but you wouldn't get a result that quickly.'

'How much does the machine cost?'

'Around $225,000.'

One in every colour please.

Dr Berger asks me to lie on the couch and starts examining my face.

'You need to exfoliate,' he says. 'And your skin is dehydrated; I saw that the minute you walked into the room. How much water do you drink?'

'Lots. I drink at least a litre of water a day.'

'Drink some more. And you should consider Botox.'

It wasn't long ago that I was Botoxed by Brenda – am I really wrinkly again already?

'Is all this Botox a good idea? I don't want to end up looking like a frying pan.'

'I believe everyone over the age of thirty-five needs Botox. But you have to keep repeating it; otherwise it is a waste of money. Botox should weaken the muscles, not paralyse them. It also prevents the formation of permanent furrows. I have sixty units of Botox in my face now,' he says, smiling and pointing to his forehead.

'Is it safe?'

'There is such a thing called the Lethal Dose 50 or LD 50. If you give the substance to one hundred lab rats then fifty will die. You are closer to the LD 50 with two aspirins than you are with Botox. So yes, it is safe.'

I don't know how he can be so categorical about it. Yes, the evidence to date, and the amounts used in treatments like these, mean I am more inclined to believe it is safe than not, but the fact is we probably won't know for years what the long-term effects of Botox are.

Dr Berger doesn't look anywhere near his age, so he must be doing something right. But I have to admit that once he tells me he is fifty-eight and I realise he can't possibly just look that way naturally, I start to question his face, look at it more critically, peering at it for signs of outside help. It's rather like a really pretty girl I met at another dermatologist's office. I thought, What lovely lips. Then she told me they were silicone and the lips immediately started to look odd to me. It's a funny thing. If someone says they look good because they have been eating well, exercising and using a new moisturiser we think, great, good for them. If they look good because they have had a face-lift, we begin to look for telltale signs of said lift, for flaws, and we conclude: That's cheating, they don't really look that good, and we think a little less of them.

Why do we mistrust cosmetically enhanced looks? Is it due to the fact that a person who tries to lie about their looks is not to be trusted? Do we view them as Dorian Gray or Faust-like characters who have made pacts with the devil and are dangerous to know? In Gray's inner circle of friends two kill themselves, one becomes, an opium addict, several are ostracised by society and another is stabbed in the neck by Gray and left to die in his attic. The more youthful and beautiful he remains, the more evil he becomes, and the more people around him end up dead, drugged or disgraced. Gretchen, who is seduced by Faust, ends up with a dead mother and brother. Then she drowns her own baby and is driven insane with grief. I think she may have concluded – at the end of it all – that it probably wasn't worth messing with him.

It could also be that people who have had stuff done often don't look quite right. The human brain is honed to recognise the human face, with all its irregularities and idiosyncrasies. Recognition starts from birth and is developed enough at two months old to activate areas of the brain. So we have years of our brains computing and digesting what a normal face looks like (unless of course you've been brought up by a cosmetic dermatologist). Think about the reaction you have if you see someone with a severely burned face. Of course, strange lips are not anywhere close, but maybe we are subconsciously reacting to something that is just not as nature intended.

Now I look at Dr Berger's face and start to wonder if his lips are real. Suddenly I see him staring at mine. He lifts up a pair of glasses from around his neck. Rather amazingly they split down the middle and then click together when he puts them on his nose. He is still staring at my lips, now through his clipping glasses. I think I see desire in his face, but can't be sure.

'I would *love* to do your lips,' he says.

CHAPTER FOURTEEN

Luscious Lips or a Trout-Pout?

Lips are one thing I have thought about constantly since I started researching this book. Partly because I've always hated mine. Consider this quote:

> She twirled around slowly, so he could see her better, proudly arching her body. It had remained very beautiful: her shoulders, arms and high, firm breasts were extraordinarily striking, despite her age, and had retained the hard brilliance of marble. But her neck was lined, and her face sagged. This, together with her dark-pink rouge, which became purplish beneath the lights, gave her an air of decrepitude that was both sinister and comical . . . She stopped talking: her lipstick had smudged at

the corner of her mouth. Slowly she dabbed it away and patiently redrew on to her ageing, shapeless lips the pure, clean arch that the years had wiped away.

This passage is from the novel *David Golder*, written by Irène Némirovsky. The main protagonist is describing his wife, a woman of a certain age. She sounds hideous and it's the 'ageing, shapeless lips' that remain for me the most potent image.

David Golder was written in 1930, when the only real options were blusher and lipstick. Nowadays you can have fake lips and tits, you can have fat grafted into your eyelids and cheeks to plump them up, you can have your fat bucal pads removed to make you look less jowly, you can have your face lifted, mini-lifted, peeled, microdermabrased, lasered and tiny injections of fillers (hyaluronic acid) injected to plump it up. You can have Botox to iron out wrinkles. And after all that you can start on your make-up.

Of all these treatments the one that most people seem to get wrong is the lips. It is very rare that you see someone with enhanced lips that doesn't look totally insane, or at best as if they've had their lips done.

There are several options for your lips: silicone,

which is permanent; any number of fillers, which last about three months; and collagen and implants such as Cosmoderm and Cosmoplast.

And apparently it's something you need to consider as soon as you hit puberty, if Dr Eva Ritvo, the vice-chairman of the Department of Psychiatry at the University of Miami Medical School, is to be believed. She is quoted in an article by Natasha Springer in the *New York Times* as saying that age fourteen is when a girl's lips reach their peak of fullness. After that it's all downhill.

The first person I ever saw with a trout-pout was related to me. I won't say who, just in case she ever reads this book. I hadn't seen her for a couple of years when we met in London for lunch. At first I thought she'd had a terrible accident. Her lips simply looked too big for her face; she looked like she'd been punched in the mouth. She must have been around sixty at the time and although the rest of her looked chic (nicely bobbed hair, Armani from head to toe, manicured nails painted a subtle neutral, natural make-up), the lips were ridiculous. This was in 1998 and the trout-pout had not yet reached epidemic proportions so I had no idea what had actually happened to her mouth, but something stopped me from asking.

It wasn't until we said goodbye that she took me to one side. 'Why don't you come with me to Nice?' she whispered. 'You could have your lips done before your wedding. It's nothing, no one will ever notice, and your lips are really too small.'

I nodded and smiled and quickly said goodbye. There were many things I wanted to do before my wedding – lose half a stone, buy some La Perla underwear for my wedding night, have a steamy encounter with Brad Pitt – but inflating my lips to ridiculous proportions was not one of them. Apart from anything else, my husband, who met this relation with me, said that if I ever did anything like that to myself he would divorce me. And we weren't even married.

My relation was probably one of the early victims of silicone-enhanced lips. In those days they were actual silicone implants. The lip was cut open and the silicone implant inserted, rather like a boob job. Now they inject silicone and therefore it is much easier to get a more natural result. But be warned; silicone is permanent so if you don't like your new lips, then tough. Also there is still one kind of silicone, although rarely used now, that sounds somewhat unsavoury. Basically, the lip enhancement is not due to the silicone oil injected, but to your body's reaction to it as it tries to defend itself from this foreign substance. The body's inflammatory response triggers the formation of collagen, which boosts the lips. The amount of collagen produced depends on your body's sensitivity to it and how pure the silicone is.

There is another type of silicone that is more widely used nowadays and doesn't create that type of reaction called Silicone 5000. Dr LookGood uses that and says he does lips in stages to make sure the client is happy. He also says it feels and looks better than the other fillers and lasts ten years, which I guess is more practical than having to come back for a top-up every few months.

'With other fillers like Restylane you get bumps, and the whole effect is not nearly as natural as it is with silicone,' he says. 'I would start very small to make sure a patient is happy and then do more if it was required. I have done literally thousands of lips. My wife has them, my ex-wife has them, my daughter has them, my assistant has them. They all look great.'

Not everybody ends up looking 'great'. Pete Burns, for example, used collagen to plump up his lips. Burns was famous for being a pop star and *Big Brother* house-guest, but now he is more famous for his disastrous lips. He is suing Dr Maurizio Veil, the man whom he claims has ruined his life by injecting his lips. Following some minor complications after treatment in 2003, Dr Veil suggested they use a product called Evolution. After repeated injections Pete suffered terrible side effects, including painful swelling, blisters, heavy discharge, unpredictable swelling to the face, inability to eat, drink or speak and granulomas (collection of chronic inflammatory cells), which meant he had pus oozing and spurting from various parts of his lips. Not a good look.

Pete has now had over one hundred surgical procedures to remove this poison from his lips. It is so bad that he has been warned he may have to have his lips amputated. It is not yet known if Evolution can be permanently eradicated.

He has described the whole experience as extremely painful and terribly detrimental to being able to lead his life. He was housebound for months and endured countless procedures. Going through this nightmare he claims has left him very depressed and, at times, even suicidal. He has gone public about these appalling experiences in the hope that it'll stop others from being subjected to a similar experience.

This is not a normal result of having your lips done. It is extreme, but worth bearing in mind.

The *New York Times* writer Alex Kuczynski also had an exploding lip and writes about it at the end of her book *Beauty Junkies*. 'Often, when I see a woman who has visibly had too much plastic surgery, I see in her face a needy quality, a desire to be loved that is never quite fulfilled, the need to be approved that is never quite met . . . I don't plan to turn into that woman. I did enough to myself to soften some edges, and I try not to regret any of those things. In fact, I did enough to make me realise how grateful I was for the existence of cosmetic surgery. Especially the exploding lip. Because it made me stop and think. And think and stop.'

You have been warned.

Fillers like Restylane, Sculptra or Evolence have now more or less replaced collagen. They are made from hyaluronic acid, which is injected and assimilated by the body so at least it vanishes after a few months.

I don't understand how so often lips are the one detail that women seem to get spectacularly wrong. I have seen hundreds of women who look like they've tried to turn themselves into Angelina Jolie. I was on holiday recently in Spain. My husband and I were sitting outside in a restaurant having lunch. At the table next door there was a family from New York. The wife was probably about thirty; she was an extremely pretty girl, with a great body, long blonde hair and green eyes. But there was something not right and after a second I'd clocked it: the lips. They were far too plump. From the side they stuck out like a spare tyre. Why would a girl ruin herself by doing something like this? You can sort of understand it when you get old, ugly and desperate, but why take a lovely face and lend it a joker-like pout for no good reason other than being greedy for more?

All that self-righteous indignation aside, I am now on my way to becoming one of those women myself. My lips have always been too small, my trout-pouty relation was right. For years I have tried to change this without resorting to a trip to Nice. I have tried lipliner around the contours of my mouth (lasts about a second) and, during the last few years, endless kinds of lip-enhancing, lip-plumping, lip-expanding lip glosses. The first one I tried promised a miracle. Bigger lips within seconds. It was called Freeze 24. And that's exactly what it seemed to do; freeze my lips. I have to admit that the effect was quite good, if a little transient, but I just didn't really like the taste or texture of it. Next I moved on to the Sexy Mother Pucker range from Soap and Glory. Just the name was enough to make me buy one in every colour. The day I bought it I had lunch with Carla and she asked if she could try it. Her reaction was rather dramatic.

'Oh my God, what have you done to me?' Her

scream shattered the quiet serenity of the Groucho Club dining room. The lip gloss had made her lips feel like they were on fire. She's all right now.

It had a less dramatic effect on me, a strange tingling sensation, which diminished the more I wore it and got used to it, but it was just too sticky. Every time a gust of wind came along, my hair would get stuck on my lips, an even worse look that thin lips. So I moved on again, this time trying Lip Fusion collagen-enhanced lip gloss. Seeing the word 'collagen' on a packet always makes me want to buy it, lack of collagen being the reason we age. Anything that gives it back to us sounds good to me. I was thrilled with Lip Fusion for the first week or so; my lips felt full and perky. But then the effect started to wear off. I still liked the colour but it just began to feel like any old lip gloss.

So what's next? Am I really willing to let Dr Berger loose on my lips, risking all the disasters I've so grimly listed above?

'Why do you want to do my lips?' I now ask him hesitantly (rather like asking a man why he wants to sleep with you. The only right answer is that he loves you. I am eager to hear what Dr Berger will come up with).

'Because I think with your big new hair and big

eyes it would be a really sexy look. Your lips are very small but you're tall so you can carry it off. It would be a wonderful thing to do to your face.'

'I really do not want to have a trout-pout,' I say, but already my 'shall I, shan't I' swing meter is rapidly going towards the 'shall I'.

'What's a trout-pout?' he asks, all innocence.

I explain.

'Oh, I've seen some horrors,' he says. 'I have a patient who is seventy and the first thing you see when she walks in the room is her lips. She had them done in the 70s with silicone and there's nothing you can do about that. No, you won't have a trout-pout. I would just put a little Restylane in your upper lip.'

'And will I look like a lunatic afterwards?'

People say that after a lip treatment your lips are swollen and you look totally mad for about three days. I am busy calculating how long I have here before I get home. I am on my way to LA after New York, where I will spend four days. Will my lips have calmed down by the time I get home? Rupert might just leave me at the airport. But if they look nice, which I'm assuming they will after the swelling has gone, he might not be too furious. He might even find me irresistible.

'They will be a little bigger to start with,' he says.

'I overcorrect by twenty per cent as you lose that in the first week. But in a week to ten days they'll be perfect. Men are going to hit on you in the street.'

Well, that could make the school run more interesting.

'And will it be permanent?'

'No, I use Restylane. I see no need to go for a permanent change. What happens if you don't like it? Restylane can last up to six months.'

'I don't know,' I say. 'Anyway, I can't do it now, I have another meeting. How long would it take?'

'About an hour. Why don't you think about it and call me on my cell later? I have a slot at 5 p.m.' He pushes his card into my hand.

I leave his office and my first thought is, Phew, what a lucky escape. Rupert will be so proud of me.

I meet my friend Sophie for a cup of tea. She congratulates me on my good sense.

'You don't look nearly as mad as I expected you to,' she says. I had warned her about the Botox, hair, pervy corset and gleaming white teeth. 'Can I see your tummy?'

I lift up my jumper to reveal the corset. I have the odd twinge of pain, but nothing serious. Although my midriff is strapped in, it feels very slim, which of course could be because it is strapped in. I also don't feel like eating very much, perhaps an aftereffect of the painkillers.

'Are you pleased with it?' asks Sophie, looking at my corset.

'I love the corset,' I say, 'but it's a bit early to tell on the tummy. They say the skin will get progressively tighter and it should feel flatter within a week once any swelling has gone down. It's a bit sore, but nothing worse than, say, a twisted ankle.'

Sophie takes a sip of her tea. 'So, what's next?'

'I am tempted to do my lips,' I say, looking at Dr Berger's card. 'And I may never get a chance again. What do you think?'

'Rupert won't like it,' she says. 'And anyway, there's nothing wrong with your lips. Mind you, there was nothing wrong with your hair or your teeth or your stomach either, as far as I can remember.'

I think about what she says. Maybe she has a point. There was nothing drastically wrong. But there was nothing drastically right either. So if Dr Berger can do for my lips what Rodolfo did for my hair, what's the downside?

'Just don't be tempted to get a boob job in LA,' says Sophie. 'I had a friend who had one done and she said it was like living with two torpedoes strapped to her chest. Her husband didn't think much of them either.'

'I won't,' I say. 'I'd never get my corset on over them.'

Before we leave the café I go to the loo. I look at myself in the mirror and put some lip-enhancing lip gloss on. I flick my new big hair around a bit. Dr Berger thinks I need bigger lips to go with it. He thinks I will look sexy. And he's not even going to charge me for the treatment. I'd love just to try it, for me and a little bit for the book. What have I got to lose? By the time I get home the lips will have deflated slightly and Rupert may not even notice. And even if he hates it, in three to six months they will be back to their normal, painfully thin selves. Just think, in an hour's time I could have luscious lips, something I have longed for all my adult life.

Outside the café I kiss Sophie goodbye and jump in a cab. I've made my choice: trembling, I dial Dr Berger's cellphone number. He answers immediately.

'Dr Berger,' I say. 'I'm on my way.'

This lip thing is not as simple as a Botox injection. It involves a lot more pain, so a lot more painkillers. The first thing I have to have is a painkiller for the painkiller. It's a cherry-flavoured gel, which tastes disgusting and had better not be colouring my newly whitened teeth. Dr Berger rubs it into my gums and then prepares the biggest needle I have ever seen for action. I have a feeling this is going to hurt.

It does. And what's worse is the feeling almost immediately afterwards. The whole area around my mouth is like a brick. It is solid and immovable. I wonder why police ever bother shooting suspects; they could just immobilise them with a dentist's injection.

Dr Berger rubs my upper lip between his fingers and asks if I can feel anything. Nothing at all. My whole lower face feels like it's been turned into cement. I suddenly feel panicked. I am immobilised, I have lost control, and a man I hardly know is about to change my appearance, possibly for the worse. What the hell have I agreed to? A scene flashes through my mind. Rupert meets me at the airport, my lips are horribly swollen. They have actually turned purple, and it's not this season's lipstick colour. He takes one look at me and a terrible look of disapproval comes over his face.

'Of all the stupid things you've done,' he sighs as he takes my bags. 'Oh, well, at least now you might get on *Celebrity Big Brother*.'

I feel like leaping up from the dentist-style chair I am in, but lack the strength. Dr Berger is unaware of my internal turmoil.

'Good,' he says, poking around my lip area with his finger. 'I am going to prepare the Restylane now.' He hands me a blue and white box with the words 'Restylane

Injectable Gel' written on it. 'You can keep this as a souvenir,' he adds. I read the contents: one syringe containing stabilised hyaluronic acid on phosphate buffered saline. And this is going into my lip? My only comfort is that it is made in Sweden. Nothing truly terrible ever comes out of Sweden. Except maybe for those outfits ABBA wore to the Eurovision song contest in 1974.

Dr Berger is hovering around me with a needle. He stares intently at my upper lip and then grabs it before injecting me. He is like a vulture, pouncing on a carcass, his movements fast and precise. This is now slightly painful and I start to panic again. Have I totally lost the plot? Are these the actions of a sane, professional woman? Possibly not, but thousands of other seemingly sane women across the world are probably doing the same thing: squirming in a dermatologist's chair as their lips are plumped up. Anyway it's too late now. As far as I can make out he works on one side and then the other. I can hardly ask him to stop in the middle of the whole thing.

Dr Berger works intensely and then announces that he's run out of Restylane.

'I need some more for your lower lip,' he tells me.

I think briefly about reminding him that he said he

would just do the upper one but have suddenly been overtaken by a kind of lethargy. There is nothing I can do and I have no real control over what happens to me in this chair. It's an odd sensation, especially for a control freak like me. Maybe this is what happens to torture victims? You feel so out of control that you just surrender. I sit patiently and wait for more torture. Rather disconcertingly I can taste blood. I am assuming it's my own.

'I burst a blood vessel, I'm afraid,' says Dr Berger, probably in response to the panicked look in my eyes. 'The lips are full of them so it's easily done. You'll have some swelling there but it will go down after a day or so.'

Great, so now I'll look even madder. What on earth was I thinking?

Dr Berger has only been injecting my lips for about five minutes, but already I feel like I want to get the hell out of there. Part of my face still feels like a block of something solid and the whole experience is not that nice. I am just hoping it's all going to be worth it in the end, and I will have lusciously kissable lips to show for my pains.

'We have a nice cupid's bow,' says Dr Berger, referring to the shape on my top lip.

'You know those two wrinkles just above my lip?' I ask him. 'Will this make them go away?' I have two wrinkles just on the top right-hand side of my lip, almost like those horrible wrinkles you see smokers getting from dragging on their cigarettes. I have been looking at them with increasing fury over the past few months. I used to smoke, but gave up shortly after university, so see no reason why I should be punished with smoker's wrinkles.

'No, but your lips will be so gorgeous, no one will notice them.'

Dr Berger has finished. He dabs my mouth with some tissue, which I see is covered in specks of blood when he throws it away, and hands me an ice pack. 'The more you can keep this on, the quicker the swelling will go down,' he tells me. 'And just dab your mouth dry, don't pull things over it.' My new lips are obviously more sensitive than my old ones were.

'Now take a look.' He gives me a small hand-mirror and I lift it slowly to my face.

'AAaaaarrgghhhhhhhhh,' is my first reaction, closely followed by shock and despair. There is a mad woman looking back at me with lips the size of a small mobile home. I look like one of those women I laugh at in the street. Except that I can't even laugh because my lips are immobile.

'Don't worry,' says Dr Berger. 'The swelling will go

down and if I didn't know you, I wouldn't be able to tell you'd had anything done at all.'

I let the mirror fall in my lap and look at him. That I just don't believe. People aren't born with lips this size. I look like I've been punched in the mouth repeatedly. Actually, I feel like I've been punched in the mouth repeatedly. Funnily enough the bigger lips also make me look as if I'm about to burst into tears. Actually, I think I am.

I am lost for words. I can't believe it. The ironic (or moronic) thing is that when I walked into his office I caught sight of myself in the mirror and thought: I don't look at all bad today, quite healthy, sun-tanned and sane. Now I just look deranged.

'In a week to ten days it will be perfect,' says Dr Berger reassuringly. 'Just keep the ice on as much as you can, and no hot drinks. They will feel like someone else's lips for about a week and then you'll start to get used to them.'

I ease myself from the chair. All I can hope is that the swelling really will go down and that I won't look like this for ever. But what if it doesn't? Could I be the next Pete Burns? I don't want to be the next Pete Burns. I didn't even like the last Pete Burns.

'You were very good and I don't even have a lollipop

I can give you,' says Dr Berger, smiling. He seems to take my devastation in his stride. But it's probably just as well he doesn't have a lollipop; I think my lips have seen enough action for a day. I tell him I want to walk back to the hotel but he says he would prefer it if I didn't, in case that accentuates the swelling, and comes outside to find a cab with me.

'I'm off to my fortieth High School Reunion tonight,' he tells me. 'Most of them look old enough to be my dad. I look at least ten years younger than all of them, I have a red Porsche and life is good.' Sounds like a breeze.

When the cab arrives I tell him he can be my first Restylane-enhanced kiss. As our pouting lips meet I wonder how ridiculous we must look; two people of a certain age with strange lips meeting for a chemically enhanced kiss. It's about as far away as you can get from Shelley's line: 'Soul meets soul on lovers' lips.' I wave to him from the back of the cab and watch him walk off to prepare for his high school reunion. He does this sort of thing every day, I remind myself, trying to quell my panic. Surely the lips will calm down and I will be able to face the world again soon. All the way back to the hotel, clutching the ice pack to my mouth, I pray that it will go down before I have to talk to anyone normal.

I squeeze the ice pack so hard it breaks and bits of a white gel-like substance fall over the back of the cab.

Of course, the swelling doesn't go down. But the odd thing is that when I arrive at the hotel I am called both honey and *mademoiselle* within the space of a minute. The doorman makes a special effort to find me a cab to take me to the airport (a scene you seldom see in New York rush-hour) and there is even a man on a rickshaw offering to take me all the way to JFK in time for my flight to LA. Maybe they think that anyone with lips this big can't possibly be interested in anything else apart from giving random men blow jobs. Or maybe my attitude has changed. Have the lips turned me into an indiscriminate flirt? Fact is, though, every time I see a mirror I think I look absolutely ridiculous. I am reminded of an interview I did with Dr Krup, the hormone specialist at HB Health in London. She once had her lips done.

'Men loved them,' she said. 'But I didn't. I hated them; I thought I looked like Daffy Duck. They just weren't my lips.'

Now I know how she feels. I don't know who these great big blubbery things belong to but it sure as hell isn't me.

I get on my plane to LA clutching my much-depleted

ice pack. At least I'm going somewhere where oversized lips are the norm, as opposed to a sign of insanity. And black corsets are always in fashion.

I'm hoping that by the time I get home and have to face my husband again, I'll look more like myself. But as we taxi down the runway and my ice pack begins to melt, a nagging voice inside my head says, what if I don't?

CHAPTER FIFTEEN

LA Women

I land in LA after a six-hour flight feeling like a wreck. My stomach is now sore. I need to lie down, I need to get this corset off, and I need to take stock of the state of my body. The thing about needles is that they tend to leave some bruising so I look a little like a battered housewife as I walk off the plane. I try to cover my face with as much hair as possible and make my way through the airport building.

As I collect my hire car (after a painful hour wait in the queue) I remember watching an episode of a TV series called *Ten Years Younger* in which they literally made people over. There was a woman featured who had extensive surgery to her face and boobs as well as liposuction. The presenter told us that she had just put her body through the equivalent of a major car crash.

Of course I haven't gone that far, but I have not been kind to my body and I am feeling the effects.

I also start to wonder when I will tell Rupert about the lips. Maybe it's safest to tell him on the phone. Or will that just give him too much time to stew and fume over my bad/mad behaviour. How much more is he going to put up with before finally telling me to get lost?

Talking of getting lost, although I am enormously cheered up by my hire car, which is red and convertible, I now have to find my way from LA airport to the Beverly Hills Hilton. I put the roof down so I can see where I'm going. Then I notice the car has a matching red and black GPRS plotter. Now you're talking. I key in the address of the Beverly Hills Hotel and we're off. Driving in LA is not as scary as it might sound. People actually drive quite slowly and the roads are vast. At one stage on Wilshire Boulevard a man tries to get into my car. I wonder briefly if I know him but then realise he's just a lunatic. Oh, well, maybe he recognised me as one of his own.

When I get to the hotel reception I notice two black men admiring the fish tank by the lifts. It is full of fish (funny that) and brightly coloured coral. What is so amusing is that one of the men had dyed his hair half orange and half yellow. In fact, it bears an uncanny resemblance to the coral in the fish tank. I bet the fish are as amazed by him as he is by them. Heaven knows what the fish think of my lips.

I go up to my room for a sleep. I wake after three hours, feeling more positive about life. After all, whatever else, I am doing well in my research for the book. Then I look in the mirror. An unsightly vein seems to have appeared in the middle of my forehead. Great, so *the* wrinkle is gone, only to be replaced by *the* vein. It is blue and threatens to stick out, really unattractive. Is my face about to turn into a version of Madonna's hands?

The lips are still swollen. They do not look like my lips at all. They still look far too big. There are also two lumps, one on the left-hand side of my bottom lip and another on my top lip, just above it. They are not immediately obvious, but I notice them. I also still look as if I'm about to burst into tears. I take off the corset and inspect my stomach. I can see swelling but other than that it looks in good shape. The scabs are healing nicely; I just hope they don't leave scars. My hair cheers me up enormously. It looks lovely: long, lush and curly.

Once I get out and about in Beverly Hills I begin to feel better. Most of the women around me look like me: they have over-sized lips, big hair and no wrinkles. They also have enormous breasts, but I'm not even going to think about that. There are limits, after all. Or are there? Yes, there definitely are. Admittedly I seem to have powered my way through most of them, but my breasts will not be surgically enhanced. At least not this week.

The anti-ageing treatments seem to be having some effect. I walk past a man sitting at a bus stop. 'You got some change to help me get a sandwich?' he asks. After a week in New York I can barely afford my own sandwich so I walk past briskly. Then he adds the words 'young lady'. I immediately turn around and give him a couple of dollars.

There is plenty in LA to amuse me. The shopping is incredible. LA is like one vast shopping mall. I drive around in my red convertible, investigating every shop I've ever heard of and wonder how anyone has any time to work here. On Rodeo Drive I see a classic Los Angeles 'Lollipop Lady' (so called due to a pencil-thin body shape with a head that seems too big for the frame stuck on top). She is wearing shoes so high they could almost be defined as stilts, a rather loose-fitting summer dress, which reveals two perfectly surgically enhanced breasts, and, of course, extra-large shades. This is another top anti-ageing tip. As your crow's-feet get worse, just buy bigger glasses. Or, even better, just wear them from the start so you don't get crow's-feet in the first place! She is standing around trying not to topple over when her designer pet, a boxer puppy, spots another dog and goes for it like a boy racer in a Porsche. Said Lollipop lady has no option but to trot along on her stilts, trying to retain her composure and not knock herself out with her enhanced breasts.

Then of course there is the obligatory lunatic. I see one that looks like Pamela Anderson in twenty years' time. (How scary a thought is that?) She is wearing fluorescent green velvet tracksuit trousers with a matching (does anything match fluorescent green velvet?) vest. Her hair (correction, someone else's hair) goes all the way down to her bottom in blonde waves. I don't even need to tell you the state of her lips (again, the fish would have recognised one of their own), the body shape (tits on a stick) or the general air of madness.

At the Nike shop on Wilshire Boulevard I see something quite depressing. An extremely pretty girl, who can't be a day over eighteen, with an older, much shorter man. This in itself is not depressing, sadly it's rather normal, but what is awful is that I can see that she has already started to 'have work', as they call it here. Her lips are too big, her hair is vast and her breasts are gargantuan. Her skin is pale and wrinkle free and I suspect it will stay that way. Somewhere under all that is what was a young pretty girl; such a shame she'll never be seen again. For her, even at her tender age, there is no way back. That is one of the key things about having surgery done. You change for ever. Do not kid yourself that you will be the same person you were. You won't. Maybe for some that's a good thing, but to me it sounds terrifying, at least where the face is concerned. Imagine looking into the mirror every day and knowing it's not really you.

Two days and twenty shopping hours after my arrival I am on my way to the celebrated Ivy Restaurant to meet my friend Lisa. The Ivy is one of those places people come to be seen. It is a very pretty place, slightly run-down maybe, and reminds me of Club 55 in St Tropez, another very fashionable eating billet. There is a lovely terrace covered in plants, tables with white linen table-cloths and waiters running around carrying mainly salads.

Rupert sends me a text message: 'Are you still alive?' it reads. 'Yes,' I respond, being careful not to trip over the entrance to the restaurant. 'All going well. Am slightly enhanced but nothing drastic and no scalpels involved.' I close my eyes as I press send. How will he react? Is my phone going to explode in a minute?

I am shown to the worst table in the restaurant. It

is indoors, practically in a cupboard, and facing the wall. Don't they know who I am? I turn my chair so I can look around. I am disappointed not to find Brad Pitt, George Clooney and at least three other film stars there tucking into their crudités. There are no celebrities at all. As far as I can make out, most people are busy looking at everyone else to see if they're famous or in disguise or even on the phone to someone famous. And talking of phones, no word from Rupert. Is he too busy seeing a divorce lawyer?

Instead of Brad Pitt behind me there is one of the most ghastly sights in the world: a woman well past her prime pretending to be twenty-five. She has so much hair, lips and tits that it is hard to make out what she looks like underneath it all. But maybe that's her aim. She is wearing denim dungarees (not a great look at the best of times on anyone other than a five-year-old) with a red T-shirt, probably Gucci or something similar. Her shoes are high and glittery, possibly Jimmy Choo. The man she is having lunch with is, I think, her husband. He looks around seventy. So not only does this woman look like an old woman trying to look young, but if more evidence of her real age was needed, she's sitting opposite it.

I know Sophia Loren modelled for the Pirelli

Calendar aged seventy-one, and I find that truly inspirational. But the fact is that once we try to look more than ten years younger than our real age, we begin to look ridiculous. The question is where does this woman go from here? When does she stop having Botox, having her lips done, hair extensions, fake nails, laser treatments to keep her skin tight and goodness knows what else? (Come to think of it, when will I?) Is there going to come a day when she suddenly puts on her oversized Chanel sunglasses and thinks, I look totally ridiculous? Or will she just go to her grave looking like a lunatic? The sad thing is, the illusion that she looks good must be working for her, or she wouldn't be doing all this. She is a classic example of the 1661. Sixteen from behind, sixty-one from the front. Actually make that 1771. And she doesn't really look young. Dr Lancer, a top Los Angeles dermatologist, whom I met in his practice on Wilshire Boulevard, says it is essential, if you're going to embark on treatments, to have someone overseeing them. 'You wouldn't build a house without an architect, would you?' he says. This woman has built her house using nothing but a bricklayer, and an untrained one at that.

But we don't have to end up like that. There are ways to avoid it, I reflect, adjusting my corset. Am I in danger of going down this route? Surely there's no harm in a bit of Botox, lip enhancement, liposuction, teeth whitening and hair extensions? All put together it does seem like rather a long list. But I am not a lunatic, unlike the woman behind me, I tell myself. I'm doing it in the interests of research.

I look around for Lisa. Still no sign of her. My stomach will be even flatter. But then how is she ever going to spot me stuck in this cupboard? I play with the pink and yellow roses on my table. They are in a teapot, such a novel idea and one I must try at home. My lips are taking a bit of getting used to. They still feel like they belong to someone else. I find myself miscalculating when I go to put something in my mouth. Drinks are the worst. Most of the contents ends up gracelessly dribbling from my mouth. When I go to the loo I check myself in the mirror to see if there's been an improvement. I still have the impression that I'm about to burst into tears. I wonder if just before one weeps one's lips get bigger? Especially when I'm tired I notice I have the on-the-brink-of-tears look constantly. Most odd. But I have been told that after a week they will have reduced in size by a third and I will feel more normal. Here's hoping, because right now I veer between thinking I look great and feeling like a silly old woman trying to look young. Which you might argue is what I am. One upside is that the unattractive smokers' wrinkles just above my lip have gone, even though Dr Berger said they wouldn't.

When I get back to my chair, I see three classic LA women walk towards the table next to me. They all have unsymmetrical faces and seem to be having difficulty walking. They sit down and start comparing handbags.

'That is a *beautiful* bag,' says one of them insincerely through a malformed mouth.

These women are more like the three freaks than the Three Graces.

I turn away from them to look at the décor. The Ivy is decorated a little like an American's idea of a French country cottage. The walls are yellow, the beams wooden. There are baskets of flowers hanging from the curtain rails and china displayed in dressers along the walls. The floor is made of terracotta tiles. On the wall next to me there is a print of the Eiffel Tower. There are shields over the window with the crest of the French Republic embossed on them. The waiters wear ties with carnations on them. Where is Lisa? I am longing to get outside to where I'm sure the action is. I still can't see any film stars but I probably wouldn't, seeing as my nose is pressed up against a wooden dresser with a large clay frog in it.

I wonder about the three graceless ones next to me. How old are they? Mid-fifties?

I've been amazed at how fake the women in LA look. But thankfully not all of them. Just after I'd arrived in LA, I met some real ones, when I was visiting part of the Mayer (as in Metro-Goldwyn) clan. Passing villa after incredible villa on the palm-lined boulevard, I imagined that they were homes to all sorts of Hollywood grandees. Just the cars parked in the drives were probably worth more than our house.

I went to see the mother of a friend of mine, Pauline, who is eighty; Florence, her sister-in-law, who is eighty-nine; and her sister, Simone, who is seventy-one.

Pauline worked as a story analyst for 20th Century Fox until her second child was born. Then she 'stayed on the mommy track' until both children had left home. After that she became a book reviewer. Florence was married to a movie producer before he died. Aged forty, she took a degree in psychiatric social work and worked at a local Beverly Hills hospital. When she retired ten years ago, she continued to counsel clients at home, and still does. Simone was a sportswear designer who retired twenty years ago. She recently started teaching at a Los Angeles fashion design school.

We all met at Pauline's house. I was slightly in awe of these women, not only because of their age, but because they have seen and done so much. Florence, who sat opposite me, looking amazing in a cream silk shirt and slacks, used to weekend with Bette Davies.

Simone arrived with some DVDs she had borrowed from Pauline: *The Last King of Scotland* and *The Good German*. They were special issues given to members of the Academy (as in the Oscars). Pauline's husband, Roger, is a member.

'It's so good to meet you,' said Simone, turning to me. 'I Googled you before I came; what fun you seem to have!' I have probably never before been Googled by a seventy-one-year-old, but then this is no normal seventy-one-year-old. Simone is slim, sprightly and extremely elegant. She was wearing a long flowing top over linen trousers. We sat down in the drawing room where Pauline had prepared a spread of tea, pecan pie and fresh strawberries.

I asked Simone how she had kept so young-looking.

'I had a mini face-lift when I was forty, which might have helped,' she admitted.

Florence also had a face-lift several years ago and believes passionately in exercising. She has been swimming for an hour a day since 1961 and has only just cut that down to thirty minutes. She also works out with a trainer twice a week. To keep her brain active she plays bridge and belongs to a book club. Her hair is blonde and cut in a bob. She told me she used to have black hair but once it started going grey she began to dye it. That worked for a while until it started going a strange red colour. 'So I started to go blonde,' she said, 'and now I like it.'

Pauline has aged more naturally than the other two. She has let her hair go grey and has never had a face-lift or anything else. She walks every day but does nothing special to keep young-looking, although she does crosswords and reads lots to keep her brain active. She's also very internet savvy. She is my only octogenarian email pen-pal.

She told me that when she worked at 20th Century Fox she was down the corridor from 'The Colonel', who was Elvis's mentor.

'Elvis used to go past my door daily and say, "Hi, ma'am",' she said. 'I was maybe two years older than him and to be called ma'am was a bit of a shock, but he was a very dear boy and of course very cute – this was way before he got all fat and disgusting.'

What these three women teach me is the importance of keeping active, not just physically, as you age. They have all had second careers late in life and I believe that has helped them to stay young. If your mind is active and interested in things then your body follows. If your brain shuts down, then it follows suit.

The other thing these ladies have shown me is that growing old is not necessarily all bad. These women don't seem depressed or angry; they seem very happy.

A friend of mine in London once said that there's absolutely no point in looking good after the age of fifty-five as 'you can't have an orgasm and you're of no use to anyone'. When I asked her what she meant she said that in a Darwinian sense we are defunct after the menopause. 'Nature doesn't need us. We should just die once we hit fifty, what's the point in us?'

I can't confirm or deny that orgasms elude us after the age of fifty-five, but I did once meet a woman in Venice who was at least sixty-five and told me she still had them. But I would argue that, orgasms or no orgasms, there is still a point to us. The author Mary Wesley, for example, wrote her first novel when she was seventy. She wrote the bestseller *The Camomile Lawn* when she was seventy-two. Margaret Thatcher was still Prime Minister when she was sixty-five. The French author Colette was still dancing on tables aged sixty. Just think of the possibilities: a table-dancing, literary Prime Minister. Is all this anti-ageing stuff because we believe deep down that there is no point to us once we pass child-bearing age? That our *raison d'être* has gone and therefore so should we? So in order not to feel useless we try to kid ourselves and those around us that we're bright young things? Perhaps we have to accept each stage of our lives and do each particular stage as well as we can. So during our sexy young stage we are just that, then we do the parenting stage and slightly stop obsessing about matching underwear and thongs and then we go on to the post-parenting stage where we try to age in the manner of Audrey Hepburn rather than the Bride of Wildenstein. But basically we take each stage for what it is and don't try too hard to stay in the one before.

Shortly before I left to come to America, Rupert and I went to a dinner party. I asked the assembled males whether they would rather be in bed with a twenty-five-year-old, a thirty-five-year-old or a forty-five-year-old. To my amazement they all said the latter. But then their wives were there and they were all the wrong side of forty. Rupert was the only one who kept quiet. On the way home I asked what age he would prefer.

'Oh, definitely twenty-five,' he said. 'There's nothing quite like a woman's body at that age, it's just beautiful. I mean, you're lovely now, but you don't look like you did aged twenty-five.'

'So you don't think I'm as sexy as I was then?'

'I didn't say that. I think you're wonderfully sexy, but your body is different, there's no denying it. And if we're discussing sleeping with strangers then I'd rather have one with a body of a twenty-five-year-old than a forty-year-old.'

I mooted the idea that there is no point to us after a certain age and he disagreed. He told me he might rather have sex with a twenty-five-year-old but he certainly wouldn't want to spend too much time with her. 'She'd probably play loud music and think *The Great Gatsby* was a hamburger,' he told me.

The conversation moved on and I told him an idea I had had for adapting a chickpea mash recipe and using rosemary or thyme instead of coriander as the books suggested.

'A younger woman would never know that,' he said. 'You see, you're a very useful person to have around.'

As I sit in the Ivy, trying not to dribble my drink through my new lips, patting my corset and flicking my hair extensions around, I reflect that we have a choice when it comes to how we age. We either go the natural route or we don't. We can accept the age we are heading into or we can hark back to one we should have left but are clinging on to for dear life. Which route am I going to take? Right now I am very much on the 'Siamese in a breeze' track, but it isn't really what I want, is it? The awful thing is, however, that the thought of going back to being just plain old me with thin hair and thin lips is depressing. I am excited by the transformations my body and face and hair have gone through; they feel rejuvenated, they make me feel attractive. But isn't it just an illusion? How real is it?

Suddenly my phone beeps. It's a message. I almost jump out of my skin, thinking it might be from Rupert. Is he still speaking to me? I can almost feel his disapproval from the other side of the world and it's making me very uncomfortable. It's from Carla. She is on her way to India to an Ayurvedic retreat. This is not the sort of thing she normally goes in for, but she's going to support a friend who needs to lose weight before an operation. She is about to take off and is nervous about the trip.

'I have seven hours in Bombay airport on my own and apparently it is v. scary,' she writes. 'Especially since I am thin, blonde and glamorous – all the things that lead to instant rape in India.' I hope she makes it to the retreat. I haven't had much experience with Ayurvedic therapies, but they are all about rejuvenating and purifying. Maybe I can convert Carla after all. I once had an Ayurvedic foot massage, which was incredible. Oddly enough it was very sexy. Normally you wouldn't associate someone fiddling with your toes as erotic (unless perhaps you were Sarah Ferguson – remember the toe-kissing scandal?) but both Mary (who also had the treatment) and I decided it was definitely among the more sensual experiences we've ever had.

'Avoid rape by scowling, something you do rather well,' I text back. 'And immediately go for the foot massage when you get there.'

What I have just put myself through is as far away from an Ayurvedic retreat as is possible to imagine. In fact I might need to go to an Ayurvedic retreat to recover. Now there's an idea. Maybe Rupert wouldn't mind looking after the children for just another week or so? But, I reflect as I rearrange the flowers on my table for the umpteenth time, arriving home with a trout-pout, more hair than Bob Marley and a surgically enhanced stomach may not make him that keen to let me out of his sight again.

CHAPTER SIXTEEN

Still Waiting for Lunch in LA

Finally Lisa shows up. She has been waiting outside for me. The manager is so embarrassed by the mix-up he gives us a table on the terrace. I say goodbye to the clay frog and walk out to join those who have been selected to lunch on the coveted Ivy terrace. I feel very special. We sit down and as I am facing the road I ask Lisa if she's spotted any stars.

'Not yet,' she says, 'but I think I see someone I once went to an acting class with.'

We order lunch. I have a vast salad with grapefruit, pineapple, pumpkin seeds and avocado. This is not the sort of thing I would have opted for before I started this book. I would have gone straight for the pasta. But something has changed.

As I start to negotiate the food in the general

direction of what used to be my mouth I realise that, rather like ageing, when it comes to putting things in your body you have two choices. You can fill it with things that are ageing or things that are anti-ageing. My lunch (if I were able to eat any of it) is anti-ageing.

According to Tina Richards, the key to anti-ageing eating is a low Glycaemic Index (GI) and a high intake of antioxidants. She is not alone in supporting this theory. Top dermatologist Dr Nicolas Perricone is among other adherents. He has developed an anti-ageing diet called 'The Dr Perricone Salmon Diet', also known as 'The Face-lift Diet'. This involves eating a low GI diet and salmon three times a day. Kate, a friend of mine, followed it for a few weeks and said the effect was amazing.

'I definitely looked younger,' she told me. 'My skin was clear and my eyes sparkled. Friends kept asking me if I was in love. But there's only so much salmon you can eat in a lifetime.'

The GI index is a system for ranking carbohydrates according to their effect on blood glucose levels. 'High glycaemic foods cause biochemical reactions in the body, which create inflammation,' says Tina. 'Although the inflammation that occurs in the skin is relatively low level, it is still sufficient to rob your skin of youth by damaging your cells, collagen and elastin.'

This is where it gets technical. High GI foods are quickly digested, thus raising levels of sugar in our blood, which triggers large amounts of the hormone insulin to be released to help to return the sugar level to normal. What happens is that when sugar bonds to collagen the fibres become stiff and lose their elasticity. The consequence of inflexible collagen is wrinkles. In addition, free radicals are created due to the inflammatory reaction described above and those free radicals in turn cause more inflammation. So a vicious cycle is perpetuating itself in your tissues.

Dr George Roman, of the Aesthetic Medical Centre in London and a specialist in nutrition and anti-ageing, confirms this in an article in *The Times* where he describes how excess sugar and insulin in the blood causes glycation where a sugar and a protein react together. This is apparently obvious in the eyes of people with diabetes. The sugar and insulin damage the eye proteins in the lens, causing cataracts. When glycation occurs in collagen it damages the collagen itself as well as collagen-producing cells. The end result is to increase the normal process of skin ageing by reducing flexibility.

But don't despair, help is at hand in the form of antioxidants. According to Tina, the top ten antioxidant-rich foods are as follows: berries (especially blueberries), green tea, turmeric and ginger (they are both rich in an antioxidant called curcumin, which Tina says is the one spice to add to your anti-ageing shopping list), brightly coloured fruits and vegetables like yellow peppers, tomatoes and carrots, dark leafy greens like broccoli, Mangosteen fruit purée (an American juice supplement you can buy online), wild Alaskan sockeye salmon, unsalted nuts like walnuts, almonds and cashews, beans (both dried and green) and apples (but never peel them).

Rather brilliantly, other foods that are high in antioxidants include dark chocolate (at least 70 per cent cocoa) and red wine. I first became aware of the latter when I met a lunatic. Well, Brian Delaney is not a lunatic, obviously, but he is the President of the Calorie Restriction Society, which believes you can increase longevity by significantly reducing the amount of calories you consume. Which I think sounds totally mad.

Members of the Calorie Restriction Society steer clear of processed foods, soft drinks, sugary puddings and white bread. They aim to keep their calorie intake down to between 1,000 and 2,000 calories a day compared with a typical intake of between 2,000 and 3,000 calories. On average we live off around 2,600 calories a day, so to go down to 1,000 would mean a sixty per cent reduction in your daily food intake. Calorie

Restriction is not an entirely new idea. Asclepius, the demigod of medicine and healing in Greek mythology, said: 'Instead of using medicine, fast.'

When we met he offered me a glass of red wine and talked to me about the benefits of drinking it. Red wine in general (and in small quantities) is known to help the prevention of thrombosis and arteriosclerosis. Resveratrol (from red grape skin) is probably the best known antioxidant in red wine and has been shown to protect against cardiac attacks as well as have anti-carcinogenic properties.

The society has around 1,400 members worldwide who all believe that self-starvation can induce physio-logical and biochemical changes in your body that slow down the ageing process. I think this should be taken with a huge pinch of salt (not many calories in that) but Brian assures me their beliefs are not without some foun-dation. Tests were carried out by the society on a group of twenty-five volunteers aged between forty-one and sixty-five. They found that they had hearts that were fifteen years younger than people of their own age eating a normal diet. The tests showed results that appeared to slow down and even reverse the ageing process by, for example, reduced inflammation and an increased produc-tion of collagen.

Meals are typically made up of 30 per cent protein, 40 per cent carbohydrates and 30 per cent fat. The idea is to get as many nutrients while consuming as few calories as possible. Personally I would lose the will to live if I had to analyse every meal to that extent, but Brian swears by it. He does look young, but he's far too thin for my liking. I can't hang out with a man whose shoulders are smaller than mine, it's too disconcerting.

I too have tried to eat my way to a younger self. Not through calorie restriction (although I once did an involuntary fast when I had to spend a night with my daughter Bea in hospital and felt totally amazing due to the fact that I hadn't eaten or drunk any wine for twelve hours) but a diet called 'The Wrinkle Cleanse Diet'. It basically involves eating lots of raw food – almost all raw food, in fact – no alcohol, no sugar, no wheat, in short nothing you'd ever really want to eat. The low GI diet Tina Richards advocates is not quite so restrictive: you can eat bread (multigrain), pasta (*al dente*, tossed in olive oil), dark chocolate and drink red wine, and it's not all raw food. 'Don't be too harsh on yourself. Try to be good 80 per cent of the time and have what you fancy for the remaining 20 per cent,' she says. Her list of total no-nos when you're being good are: animal fats (so butter is out for a start), hydrogenated fats and oils (which means heat-damaged fats and oils), white bread (try telling a Frenchman to live without his baguette), doughnuts (would I ever?), white bagels, white rice, instant rice, quick-cook porridge, rice cakes, crisps, sugar, sucrose, fresh orange juice (I know, I was amazed too, but it's the high sugar content – if you want juice then go for berry smoothies), potatoes in large portions, full-fat dairy products, red meat, all spirits and ready-made meals high in preservatives. I did have to question Tina about the white rice thing. I mean, which women would you say age best in the world? Yes, the Asians. They seem to look twenty until they're about eighty and then one day they wake up and look about 1,000 years old. And how much white rice do they eat?

'Glycaemic load is the total GI sum of all the foods in one meal,' says Tina. 'Low GI food combined with a high GI food can make a total medium GI meal, depending on the portions of each. In reality Asians tend to have a small bowl of rice with their meal (unlike Westerners who have a plateful) and they eat a large amount of vegetables. Asians also eat a lot of fish, which is low GI and anti-ageing. And they drink a lot of green tea.' If you do want to eat rice try the brown basmati rice, which has a much lower index.

So, back to my wrinkle-cleanse diet. I felt great, my

skin looked great, I slept well and although *the* wrinkle was still there at the end of the week I could see the huge benefits of it. But I got so *bored*. I was fed up with having to think about every damn thing I ate. And when you can't eat lots of things you end up totally obsessive. I would hardly finish breakfast before I was planning lunch and dinner. I convinced Rupert to join me for two days. He did two days, pronounced himself jolly pleased with the results and then went and opened a bottle of wine. It was torture to watch him drink it. I was miserable. The fact is, you could, and probably should, adopt this kind of detox as a way of life but I think you will lose the will to live if you do. And become a bore. My motto is everything in moderation. Particularly moderation.

We all know that diet is essential to staying young and one of the key factors in environmental ageing. I remember a feature at the Science Museum in South Kensington when I went with the children a couple of years ago. They projected the image of a young child on the wall, then showed in a series of images how this child would look aged thirty on a good diet and exercise. The film then cut to how the child would look on a diet of fatty foods and sugar. It was like a completely different person. Just as the sun damage your children get at an early age is the most harmful thing to their skin in later life, so their diet is crucial during their formative years.

Purely for cosmetic gain, Dr Frederic Brandt, a leading Miami-based dermatologist, says that cutting out sugar is the best thing you can do. 'It can knock ten years off your face. Sugar hastens the degradation of elastin and collagen,' he says. 'In other words, it actively ages you.'

At his suggestion I tried 'The Brandt Cleanse', which entails eliminating sugar, wheat and dairy for thirty days. I did very well for three. With three small children and a wine-loving husband, thirty days of eating sprouts just didn't work, but I am sure it's one of those things that once you get into it you'd love it. Dr Brandt says he is totally hooked and to him anything with sugar tastes horribly sweet. Now that I eat dark chocolate I can see how he feels. Milk chocolate tastes really sugary.

Dr Brandt has also come up with a miraculous little thing called the Antioxidant Water Booster, which helps repair the skin and 'slow future signs of ageing from the inside out'.

My favourite is the green tea version. One drop is the equivalent of fifteen cups of green tea; you simply add it to water or juice (not orange juice, obviously). You can get it at Space NK in London or online. Water itself is an essential factor, of course. It is the most essential thing; we can survive without food for weeks, but not without water. And purely on a cosmetic level, as I have mentioned, you must moisturise from the inside out. I drink water all day long. I carry a bottle with me even if I'm just doing the school run. I have water on my desk all day. I feel better the more I drink, but you find what suits you best. Water is one of the things every anti-ageing guru across the globe will tell you to pour down your throat in vast quantities. Except Tina, who says you should drink some, but all this two-litres-a-day mantra is nonsense. 'You get so much water through your foods,' she says. 'There is no need to drink incessantly.' One mineral water from Scotland, called Deeside, was hailed as having anti-ageing properties, though no one could really explain quite how. Another brand, called Aqua Bimini, was marketed as the first anti-ageing water because it contains quinic acid, which is said to repair DNA. On their website they explain that the length of your lifespan is determined by how fast your body can repair DNA, hence the anti-ageing element. All the oxidants you expose your body to damage your DNA, which leads to ageing. I haven't tried the water, but they claim that after thirty-three days of drinking it, DNA repair is increased by 30 per cent. Sadly it seems for the moment it's only available in South Africa. And going there may increase your chances of being shot by about 400 per cent, so it may not be worth it. Stick to plain old tap water instead. All the studies I have read comparing tap and mineral water say there is no difference and in some the tap actually comes out on top. Water is, of course, cleansing, which is key to staying young.

Liz Brewer, whom I met at an anti-ageing conference and who presents the TV show *Ladette to Lady*, says, 'Anti-ageing is all about cleansing. You can't paint a new picture on an old canvas. People are more and more into eating foods that are not helping to generate more cells, then wonder why their hair is not glossy, why their children are bad-tempered, why they're tired all the time.'

Liz eats almost 100 per cent raw food and swears by sprouts and wheatgrass. An important tip, though, is to drink it on an empty stomach. 'It acts a bit like an oven cleaner,' says Liz, 'so it will clean up whatever you have in your stomach.'

I ask Liz if she drinks alcohol. 'Yes, champagne,' she replies. She looks very good on it.

All these theses and ideas make sense to me, some more, some less so, and I am inspired by people who eat healthily constantly. But, I have to say, I find it impossible to do it myself at all times. There are moments when I really want a scone with clotted cream on and

I'm not going to stress myself out by denying myself everything all the time. I once met a very thin Parisian. I asked her if she watched what she ate. She took hold of my arm and looked deep into my eyes. 'I haven't had a croissant for thirteen years,' she said.

So here's my compromise. Don't become too dull, but do think about what you eat and if you can choose the healthier option. If you're in a restaurant go for the salad, not the burger and chips. If you happen to be in Italy and you're desperate for an Italian ice cream, go for blueberry flavour (packed with sugar, but also antioxidants and delicious). Don't just eat for the sake of eating – we really don't need all the food we stuff into ourselves every day. Sometimes hunger pangs are actually a sign of dehydration and so you may just need to drink a glass of water. If you must snack, then buy some dried fruit or nuts – almonds are especially good for you. Or try oatcakes. If you can, change your coffee and tea-drinking habits for something that actually does you good.

Rupert's grandmother Kitty used to drink hot water every morning and every evening. I do the same. It's amazing how addictive it becomes. If you can't face raw water then add some lemon (very detoxing) or some rosemary (good for clarity of thought) or even some honey if you need a boost. Although honey is really just sugar. My favourite drink by miles is green tea. It is full of antioxidants and essential in the battle against ageing. I've started drinking about three pints of it a day. Rupert is in despair. 'You're going to live for ever,' he says, 'and irritate us all for decades to come.'

Go for olives with the aperitif, not crisps, and eat a square of good dark chocolate instead of a Mars bar. It should be a minimum of 70 per cent cocoa, but I actually like the 85 per cent variety. It might taste bitter to begin with but once you get used to it anything else tastes too sweet.

Finally, remember that red wine with resveratrol is incredibly good for you, so don't go for more than a few days without it. And if you feel like you're putting on weight or overeating, try to change your routine.

When I came back from a trip to London where I slightly overindulged (mainly Carla's fault, of course, who insisted on resveratrol in large quantities for both lunch and dinner) I went on a forty-eight-hour fruit diet and was back to normal straight away.

And remember, it is also possible to change things, even if I can't seem to do it consistently. Heather Bird, for example, follows a strict regime that has now become second nature. For her, the most important thing to stay young is nutrition.

'It's very true that you are what you eat,' she says. 'You should think about everything you put into your body. When I wake up, I first have wheatgrass, then I wait twenty minutes and have a juice.'

Heather has a different 80/20 rule from Tina. She suggests that if you possibly can, you should eat 80 per cent raw food and 20 per cent cooked. This is next to impossible during the winter, but during the summer it can be done.

'Don't you ever eat a biscuit?' I ask.

'I am now so pure that if I do eat bread or a biscuit I can see it in my face. I get puffy eyes. During a conference recently I drank coffee too and my skin became really dry and I broke out in acne. But for most people they are so full of toxins they don't even notice. People are immune to it, they are so desensitised. My husband, for example, has a stability in his lack of health. So when he has a massage that moves the toxins he starts to feel uncomfortable.'

'So your husband hasn't followed your example?'

'No, sadly not.' She smiles. 'He tried to for a while. Since he's known me he quit smoking three times, but clearly part of him wants to smoke. It's unfortunate because I'm in this business and it would be great if my husband could live it and be a great role model. The few times he did live it he lost weight and looked better, and everyone said: wow, what are you doing? And he said: 'I'm going to Heather's clinic.' But he is a lot better than he was. He doesn't drink like he used to and watches what he eats, but still smokes.'

'Do you drink?'

'Not really.'

'But isn't some alcohol, such as red wine, actually meant to be good for you?' I ask, desperately hoping she will say, 'Yes, having a hangover is in fact the real secret of eternal youth.'

'One or two glasses of wine a day, yes, but to be honest, for me that's too much, it just doesn't work for me.'

Nowadays there are specific food supplements that are geared to anti-ageing. I bought one about two years ago for a vast amount of money and it is still sitting in my fridge. It is a powder you're meant to eat a teaspoon of a day. It tastes so vile I think I would rather age than eat it.

Tina is not big on supplements. She thinks you should get most of your nutrients through your diet, so her tips to boost an anti-ageing regime are part of the diet itself. One is to have a tablespoon of concentrated tomato paste a day to boost your skin's natural protection against UV rays. Another is a small glass of red wine high in resveratrol, such as Cabernet Sauvignon or Pinot Noir, along with dark chocolate, green tea and a couple of tablespoons of extra virgin olive oil to improve your intake of essential fatty acids.

I have started popping a lot of vitamins since I began researching this book, mainly because Dr Berger in New York told me he takes about forty pills a day.

That sounds a little excessive to me. How does he have time to work?

'What do you pop?' I asked him at the time, slightly baffled.

'Vitamin C, DHEA, calcium (with magnesium so I don't get constipated), multivitamins with minerals, vitamin E, chromium picolinate, lecithin, fish oils . . .' The list went on.

I have not become as obsessive as Dr Berger, but I do now try to take fish oils, multivitamins with pro-biotics, vitamin C, vitamin B, calcium (no magnesium and all is fine, thanks) and evening primrose oil. Of course, more often than not I forget to take them all so instead of once-a-day they have become once-a-week but they might be doing some good.

The other thing I tried is the skin supplement Imedeen. It is expensive and although I took it for three months I can't really tell whether it's made a difference. But there is clinical evidence it can be beneficial to photo-damaged (sun-damaged) skin at the dermis level, improving the basic texture and skin structure as well as the skin's ability to retain moisture.

I finish off my salad. The crowds of nobodies are beginning to head for the valet parking. Lisa and I get up to go. I feel a slight twinge in my stomach. Maybe there is no longer room for food. Lisa catches sight of my corset.

'What's with the kinky underwear?' she asks.

I explain the SmartLipo.

'You look very LA,' she says. 'Are you sure that look is going to go down well back in Europe?'

I am saved from confronting the answer by my phone beeping. It is a response from Rupert. 'Do I need to start buying you bigger bras?' it reads.

'Not yet,' I respond. 'I have luscious pouting lips.'

There is silence for a few tense minutes.

'Do they look good?' he responds.

I make a mental calculation. Dr Berger said they would be perfect in a week's time. So far they have had three days. I will be home in another three days. That's almost a week.

'Yes,' I text back. 'You'll love them.'

CHAPTER SEVENTEEN

Laughing on Laguna Beach

Nothing could have prepared me for this. I am on Laguna Beach in southern California, running down towards the sea, clapping my hands and barking at a sea lion. I am not doing this alone, in fact had I been alone, the appearance of a sea lion might not have provoked such a reaction. I would probably just have looked at it and thought, Oh, how nice, a sea lion.

But today I am with the Laguna Beach Laughter Yoga Club and when one of the club members starts racing towards the sea lion like a lunatic, the rest follow. And actually you'd feel more of a fool staying behind on your own than following the crowd.

I first came across the Laguna Beach Laughter Yoga Club on the internet. I keyed in Los Angeles and anti-ageing and up it popped. Laughter is no laughing matter when it comes to ageing and has more things to recommend it than most. Botox will do your brow, SmartLipo your buttocks, but what else can boast to activate the immune system, destress you, be good for your cardiovascular system (another name for laughter is internal jogging), lower your blood pressure, reduce pain, increase stamina, fight depression and make you look good by giving you a healthy, happy glow all at the same time? In addition, the release of endorphins laughter causes gives you a general sense of wellbeing. Indirectly stress is our number-one killer; it affects us physically and mentally, and there's no doubt that laughter alleviates stress.

These are not just opinions voiced by the Laguna Beach Laughter Yoga Club as an excuse to act like lunatics on the beach every morning; they are scientific facts, results of controlled experiments carried out by, among others, Dr Lee Berk of the Loma Linda University in California, whoever he might be. But he is not the only one. It was an article published in the Journal of the American Medical Association that finally made people think about laughter as a medical tool. The article was entitled 'Laugh If This Is a Joke' and was written by a Swedish researcher (the Swedes are not renowned for their great sense of humour) called Lars

Ljungdahl. He confirms that laughter has an immediate symptom-relieving effect on patients with chronic problems and that the effect is increased if they laugh regularly over a long period of time. Therefore a so-called 'humour therapy programme' can increase the quality of life in chronically ill patients.

As children we laugh an average of four hundred times a day. As adults it decreases to around fifteen. In 1995, a Bombay-based doctor and yoga student called Madan Kataria had a flash of inspiration at four o'clock in the morning. 'I was a stressed doctor, working all hours and had just written an article about the benefits of laughter for a health magazine,' he tells me. 'Then all of a sudden I got it. I realised that we just don't laugh enough. I said to myself: I need to laugh more.'

He decided to create laughter clubs. 'People thought I was crazy,' he says. 'But eventually I found four others to join me.' They started off by telling jokes but soon found they wore thin.

'After ten days we ran out of jokes so I said let's just fake it. Our bodies can't tell the difference between fake and real laughter so the benefits are the same. In fact, the fake laughter made us all laugh properly.'

Now there are eight Laughter Leaders (trained by Dr Kataria) throughout the world and the idea is gaining in popularity. There are a total of 5,000 laughter clubs in 53 countries (see www.laughteryoga.org for more information). Most of them are in India (3,500) where they meet up to eight times a day: four times in the morning, twice at lunchtime and twice in the evening. Dr Kataria begins every day with laughter. In fact, he seems to laugh all the time. I had a twenty-minute conversation with him and he must have laughed at least ten times, which then made me laugh, so I guess it is catching.

I decide to find out more. If all there is to not ageing is laughing I could save a fortune on creams and treatments. I'll be laughing all the way to the bank. I email the Laughter Yoga Club and after a few days receive a charming response from the founder, Jeffrey Briar. He signs off his emails with things like, 'Joy, love and laughter' or 'Myriad blessings' or 'Giggles and wiggles', and calls me 'my dearest Helena'. We have a lovely long correspondence as we plan my trip to Laguna Beach. At one stage he says he looks forward to 'laughing' with me. It begins to feel like an internet romance.

I'm not sure why but I expect to see a huge gathering of people when I show up at the beach, a little later than scheduled due to horrendous traffic. So I walk on to Laguna Beach and look for said crowd. There is no one. Am I in the right place? This is definitely Main

Beach. Jeffrey told me they meet by the restrooms, so where are they? I start walking up the beach and suddenly see a man waving at me. I assume this is Jeffrey but I am in California so you can never be too sure. As I approach him I see a large sheet laid out on the sand with Laguna Beach Laughter Club written on it. But where are the laughing masses?

'Welcome,' says Jeffrey, hugging me warmly and kissing me on both cheeks, then pulling forward another man. 'This is Dave, one of our group leaders.'

I shake Dave's hand; after all we've had no internet romance.

Jeffrey is younger than I expected. Correction, he looks younger than I expected. He is fifty-two but looks no more than forty, more evidence, if it was needed, that laughter is the way forward. He is wearing a faded red T-shirt with a laughing sun on the front and 'Laguna Beach Club' on the back, and loose-fitting trousers. He has brown-blond hair, cut short, and a face with a lot fewer laughter lines than I expected. He's nice-looking, but, more than that, has an aura about him that is, well, just lovely really. He's a man you feel you can trust immediately, which is unusual in itself. He so obviously just wants to help people and make them happier.

The rest of the group starts to arrive. First up is

Cathy, a thin, pretty woman aged around forty-five, with wispy blonde hair, wearing a large straw hat and apricot-coloured trousers and top. She reminds me of a member of the Bloomsbury set, if a little more yogified. I notice she takes it all very seriously, closing her eyes and breathing deeply, at one with nature. In fact it might be Cathy that starts the run towards the sea lion; she is very good at spotting creatures in the sea.

Maria, Effie and Laurel are next, followed by Kevin, a large man who has a slightly military air about him. I wonder if he's a marine, but at the laughter club it isn't seen as the done thing to quiz people about what they do. Everyone is extremely jolly and welcoming. The class is as far away from a snotty London exercise studio as you can get; everyone seems genuinely delighted to see me and there is a real feeling of happiness.

'Welcome, everybody. Since we have a new friend this morning I'll go through the introductory stuff,' says Jeffrey. 'This is Helena, she's from England.'

This last piece of information is greeted with cheers. This is something they do a lot. Anything can be an excuse to cheer, from a statement like 'the sun is shining' to the council worker men driving past us in their four-wheel drive to maintain the beach, to a dog having a pee on a nearby tree.

'At the Laguna Laughter Club we practise laughter as a form of exercise, like thousands of laughter clubs around the world,' begins Jeffrey. 'We don't tell jokes, we don't watch funny movies, we just practise laughter for its own sake. The laughter might start fake, but it becomes real laughter because we keep our eyes open and look at each other. We're like little kids going to the playground; we leave all that judgemental stuff behind. We laugh from another place here. Laughing at jokes is fine, that's great, but here we laugh with the wisdom of the body. You don't even have to feel like laughing, it'll come.'

I am intrigued as to how this collection of people is suddenly going to start doubling up with laughter without anyone cracking a joke, or at least falling over. When I told my husband what I was doing he said: 'Are they going to laugh at you because you can't touch your toes? Is that why they invited you along?'

Just the place is enough to make you want to smile, at least. It is a very pretty beach, not vast, but with smooth sand and some rocks out to the right, gradually vanishing into the water. The whole area has a very well-kept feel to it; the grass between the beach and the road is perfectly mowed, the wooden buildings on the beach are clean and the paintwork fresh. The sound of the waves lapping the shore almost drowns Jeffrey's voice out. It is a perfect day; sunny and warm. Jeffrey tells me it is rarely too cold to do the class and if it rains they go under a gazebo further along the beach.

We begin with some warming up exercises, lifting up our arms, breathing in and out.

'One of our rules is no new aches or pains,' says Jeffrey. 'So if anything I say causes you pain, don't do it.'

We open and close our hands, rotate our wrists, bend forwards and backwards, rotate the shoulders; but still no laughing.

'Now we're going to start warming up the voice. Do circles with your knees together, making the sound of oooh,' says Jeffrey.

We all do as he says, sounding a bit like a gaggle of fake ghosts. This is at least beginning to feel silly. Is it too early to giggle?

'Now let's circle the pelvis to the sound of oh.'

Then we move the ribcage around to the sound of aaah. Everyone seems to enjoy this one; the aahhs get louder and louder, towards the end they sound like expressions of relief or even ecstasy. We circle the head to the sound of any noise we like and for some reason most of the group picks on one that sounds rather like you're being sick. I think the idea is to expel all the old air. I do the best I can and enjoy expelling the LA traffic-jam air and substituting it for Laguna Beach freshness.

'Now let's do a t'ai chi swing,' says Jeffrey. 'Let your eyes just focus on what they want of the beautiful view as you move round. Great. Now for some breathing exercises. Breathe in through the nose and breathe out all the old air.' Again the sick-making noises – it's quite good fun, actually. Not the sort of thing you ever do, and it really does make me feel like I'm cleaning out my lungs.

'There is no better air anywhere than when water droplets are breaking and releasing their energy,' says Jeffrey. 'OK, so now we'll do the same breathing exercise, but on the out-breath we'll laugh. Keep your eyes open, look at the other people, here we go.'

I breathe in and wonder how on earth I'm going to be laughing a few seconds from now. Amazingly, I am. It starts off fake, but Jeffrey is right, when I see everyone else laughing, I start laughing too, it's contagious. I mean they all look so silly, and so do I.

With each breath the laughing becomes more raucous. It lasts for about thirty seconds and then Jeffrey cuts us off and we breathe in again. After five times or so my cheeks are already hurting, which I suppose shows how little I laugh normally.

Next we have to maintain eye contact with someone and laugh until Jeffrey tells us to stop. I find this one a bit trickier; it feels unnatural, and of course there is that rational voice in my head saying, 'What on earth are you doing? Have you any idea how stupid you look?' But I try to throw myself into it and laugh as much as I can. Although I have to admit it's a relief when Jeffrey finally tells us to stop. He is amazing at it, by the way; he laughs all the time, a proper, deep, honest laugh.

The next exercise involves showing others our hands and laughing at them. Funny how you can find hilarity in anything. After a while you really start to believe that there is something funny in the palms of someone's hand and it makes you laugh.

'OK, let that one go,' says Jeffrey. 'Bring your hands together and clap. This is something we'll do throughout: ho ho ha ha ha, ho ho ha ha ha.' We clap our hands and say ho ho ha ha ha to the rhythm.

'I love the way people over in England say ho,' says Jeffrey. 'It's so refined. By the way, this is something Laughter Yoga people all over the world do, so if you're ever like in Turkey and you see someone doing this, right away you'll have a friend, no matter what language they speak.'

Next we do the measuring-laughter exercise. This

involves imagining you are measuring your arm with a tape measure that you hold in your other hand and it culminates in laughter. This gets the biggest laugh so far. They're really cracking up now and I am cracking up at the sight of them cracking up, so I suppose it's working.

Every so often we break into a ho ho ha ha ha, which is a welcome relief for my aching cheeks.

'A whale,' shrieks Cathy suddenly. Everyone cheers and claps and waves at the creature, which immediately takes cover. Then it's back to the serious business of laughing.

Next, other so-called group leaders lead an exercise. Effie takes command and instructs us to do the lawn-mower. This consists of trying and failing to get a lawn-mower started and then on the third go succeeding and breaking into fits of laughter. I find this one really tough, and, believe me, I am trying to leave my rational self behind. But just as I am about to get revved up (or rather my non-existent lawn-mower is) three of the most beautiful men I have ever seen walk by. They are lifeguards, wearing tight navy-blue shorts and T-shirts with 'Laguna Lifeguards' written in white on the back. Their shoulders are broad, their waists slim, their perfect features chiselled and here I am, laughing hysterically at an imaginary lawn-mower. It's not a good look. (My LA friend and Pilates teacher Constance tells me later that all the model scouts come to Laguna Beach to look for talent because everyone there is so beautiful. What a great job – why didn't I ever think of that? I suppose the downside is you have to look for stunning women too, whereas I usually try to avoid them.)

'Dolphins,' shouts Cathy. Even the passing of the lifeguards isn't as magical as this. I have never seen dolphins free in the sea, it is just enchanting. They dive in and out of the water in perfect synchrony, like ballet dancers in the chorus. We all stand and gaze at them for a while, then it's back to the laughing business, but not before Cathy has been acknowledged for her contribution to the group by a chorus of, 'Very good, very good, yeeeeaaaah!' and clapping.

Next up is the so-called gibberish punch line. We all breathe in and one person says a word in gibberish, which we all laugh at. Jeffrey goes first and makes a silly noise. Everyone cracks up. Then we go round the circle. 'Obviously we're not laughing at what's been said,' says Jeffrey. 'We're doing proactive laughter, not reactive laughter.' This notwithstanding, I am now panicking as my turn approaches. What the hell do I come up with? I'm a writer, for goodness' sake – is it possible that I can't think of a thing to say? I think about the silliest word I know and spurt out 'gobbledegook'. It seems to have the desired effect. After this exercise we do another ho ho ha ha ha and then a yeeeeaaaaah, very loudly and happily.

The relaxation is next and it is lovely. We all lie with our heads in the middle of the large sheet, feet out, in a large circle. Jeffrey talks us through our body parts and tells us to relax each one in turn. And then, just as I think the laughing is over, he tells us all to laugh silently for two minutes. This is easier than you might think, especially when you're lying there thinking how daft you must look.

'Congratulations,' says Jeffrey after the relaxation. 'You now have the power to be free of stress whenever you want.'

After the relaxation we all sit round in a circle. It's as close to being in a commune as I have ever come. It is odd, and it's going to sound very new-age, but there is a feeling of peace and belonging. Maybe it's the beautiful surroundings, the dolphins swimming away, the sound of the waves, the hilarity of the laughter, I don't know, but I feel very good. Or maybe it's just relief that the laughing is over, rather like the end of an aerobics class.

'Put your hands on your heart. We're now going to

share our happy hearts,' says Jeffrey. Oh, help, I think, just as it was all going so well, it's now gone totally silly. 'Begin by imagining someone to whom you'd like to send some good energy. It could be a person, a country, an idea; it could be yourself if you feel like you could use some more positive energy right now. Now push your hands away from your hearts and send all that good energy for peace and wellbeing out to the person or place you're imagining.'

I imagine Iraq where a car-bomb has just gone off in the book-buying district of Baghdad.

'Now, if you're willing, raise your arms and send these thoughts out to all beings, everywhere,' says Jeffrey. 'Let there be health, peace and joy everywhere.'

I do as I'm told, everyone apart from Claire Booth, who pinched me till I bled at primary school. Why on earth should I help her? Robert Mugabe is also excluded.

After this, I ask all of the group members to say a few words about why they come here and what they get out of it.

Cathy tells me she has been 'laughing regularly' since 2005 and that she comes pretty much every day. 'I come because I love to laugh and it connects me to nature and the people here. It's a lot of fun. I have less stress in my life and I literally haven't gotten a cold or gotten sick since

I started. It's amazing. I have less anxiety in my life too. Obviously I still have it but I get away from it much faster. I love it; I wish everyone would give it a try.'

Laurel, a woman aged around fifty, who for me epitomises a hippy-style southern Californian, with wild dyed hair, lots of layers and scarves, says she has experienced 'cellular joy' deep in her cells, which has helped her to 'youth' rather than age. 'I am not ageing, I am in the process of "youthing",' she says. 'I recently had a stroke and the Laughter Club has helped enormously with my healing and recovery.'

Kevin, the one who looks like a marine, explains that he was clinically depressed before the laughter yoga. It's very odd to see such a macho man open up about himself; he really does look like he'd be more at home in the SAS. 'I have no more feelings of depression, whereas before I was always depressed on the inside but people on the outside would never know it. The negative feelings are gone and life is positive.' Everyone cheers and claps. Kevin continues. 'I decided to do this for twenty-one days because I heard if you do something for twenty-one days it becomes a habit. And that was forty or fifty days ago. But the thing I believe most is that your body doesn't know the difference between fake and real.'

He tells the story of a friend who was depressed. He told her to wake up every morning and remember a time when she was in love. Then he told her to pretend to be in love: walk down the street like you're in love, look in the mirror like you're in love, people give you hell at work and you just laugh at them and say, 'You must not be in love.' Kevin says they would call each other once a week to monitor her progress. After a few weeks, his friend came out of her depression and it turned her life around. As Kevin says; 'Your mind can re-create whatever joy you want.'

David leads the group on Wednesdays and Fridays. He says he used to have a lot of pain in his joints, which has gone now, and that he was always a bit of a loner and now has a lot of friends. 'I don't think I've ever been happier. And I'm now able to look stupid in a public place without worrying.'

Maria has only been coming for two days but says she loves the fact that she can become a child again.

'It's never too late to have a happy childhood,' says Jeffrey, smiling broadly.

Effie is a retired friend of Jeffrey's mother. She is probably in her sixties, has grey curly hair and wears jeans and a green long-sleeved T-shirt. She says the club has filled a space in her life and given her day a structure. She started a year or so ago. 'I was also always worried about making a fool of myself. I hesitated a little bit; but it only took me five minutes to relax and get into it. Last birthday someone asked me, how was your last year? I told them from the bottom of my heart, this was the best year of my life. I can't attribute all of it to this, but a big part of it was this gathering.'

After the class Jeffrey and I go for a coffee. He tells me that when he did the training with Dr Kataria he saw for himself the benefits of it and made a commitment to laugh every day for forty days so that it would become a habit. 'I experienced the pleasurable effects and when I had a stress reaction I could very quickly get rid of it as soon as I could laugh somewhere,' he says, tucking into a poached egg on a croissant (yes, even the waitress was shocked). 'All of my stress has gone. And on a personal level one of my favourite benefits is socialisation. I see people who have no one, like widows and lonely old people, who come along and for them it's a total lifeline, it's wonderful. This pure, innocent joyfulness is nice at any age.'

'But how can you just laugh if something awful happens?' I ask him.

'I wait for an appropriate moment,' he says. 'Obviously there are times when you just can't laugh, but if you're in a stressful situation and in public you can do this . . .' And quick as a flash he whisks out his mobile phone, flips it open and laughs hysterically into it. He even points to it and shows it to our neighbouring tables. The amazing thing is that by now I am laughing and so are the people sitting close to us.

Jeffrey slams the phone shut. 'Thank you for sharing that moment of laughter with us,' he says to the people around. They lap it up.

Jeffrey, who has been a yoga teacher for thirty-four years, is trying to get approval from the American state to hold state-funded laughter yoga classes along with his yoga classes to improve people's health. He thinks it's only a matter of time before laughter yoga is taken seriously. I think in terms of medication the American medical authority could (and does) support a lot worse. After all, it can't do any harm, it's practically free (Jeffrey doesn't charge for his beach classes) and from what I've seen it does a lot of good.

Viewed as a pure anti-ageing technique, unlike Botox, laughter yoga is not one of those things you can easily measure, but here's what I know: Jeffrey looks and is great. After the class I felt fantastic, more relaxed and happier than I have done for ages. I mean truly relaxed, to the extent that all I wanted to do was hang out on the beach and listen to the waves. This is not a normal occurrence for me – I am usually unable to sit down. I can't even watch television sitting down, I have to be ironing or doing yoga or sit-ups or painting my nails at the same time. But I felt extremely Zen after my morning on Laguna Beach and if you think about stress as our number-one killer, waking up in the morning, wandering along to the beach and laughing while you watch dolphins swim side by side has got to be anti-ageing.

Of course we don't all live in Laguna Beach, but the lesson I learned from Jeffrey is this: find something that makes you happy and releases tension, and do it. And when you get stressed think about laughing instead of letting it get to you. Life's too short to get wound up. As Abraham Lincoln said: 'With the fearful strain that is on me night and day, if I did not laugh I should die.'

The next evening I board my flight home. I try (in vain) to use my new lips to flirt my way to an upgrade. They have calmed down and I am growing used to them. I dribble a lot less and also no longer look like I'm about to burst into tears. But I am still not 100 per cent sure about them. I have that feeling when you try on a dress that isn't quite there but you're still tempted to buy it.

You rearrange it around your hips, imagine it with a scarf and wonder if it will ever work. I feel the same about my lips. Although they now look normal-ish, I'm not sure they're a good fit. My stomach, however, looks and feels good. The corset has come off and the swelling has gone down. I wouldn't say there is a huge difference but it certainly feels and looks a little flatter. I think one of the problems is that you get used to your body very quickly, whatever shape it is, so maybe the flatter stomach has crept up on me and not bowled me over, unlike my teeth and hair. I'm still mad about them. Every time I smile I still feel dazzling. And I just can't get enough of my long locks.

As I settle in for a sleep I wonder what Rupert will think. What, if any, part of the new me will he like? Will he think I look younger, or just dafter? The afternoon before I left LA I had a rather sobering experience that made me realise that despite all my efforts, there is still one thing eluding me – actual youth.

I went for a walk on Venice Beach. As a beach it has little to recommend it except its sheer scale, and along the sidewalk are some of the most unsavoury shops you can imagine, but it is lively, filled with all kinds of different types of people rollerblading, windsurfing, running, kissing. It's a kind of microcosm of Los Angeles all packed into one area. I was walking towards the sea when an incredibly sexy young man came towards me. He was wearing a wet suit and carrying a surf board. As he approached he began to peel off his wetsuit to reveal a perfect torso, not too big, well toned, muscular, and a beautiful brown colour. By the time he sauntered past me his wetsuit was hanging casually around his hips. He ran his hand through his black, thick, wet hair and glanced at me. He really was to die for. Bright blue eyes and fine features. For a moment I forgot that I am married with three children and flashed him a smile. He frowned and looked away. This was a defining moment for me. I realised that while I would be perfectly happy to make a pass at this man, he was probably thinking: There's some chick about my mother's age giving me the eye, how disgusting; astounded to think that someone of my age had a sex drive at all, let alone have the warped imagination to think I could sleep with him. It reminded me of something my friend Annika said when I told her I rather liked the look of the son of some friends of ours who was staying with us once.

'Pounce on him,' she said, 'but he'll probably scream and tell you he's calling his parents, followed by the police.'

I headed into a bar for a drink to cheer me up. There

was country music blaring from several speakers. Posters on the wall declared 'Pop Music is the Enemy'. Lucky I wasn't wearing my Take That T-shirt. I was *so* out of my comfort zone but consoled myself with the fact that there were millions of neural pathways being created listening to the music warbling away in the background. As I sat at a table a giant waiter came lumbering towards me.

I ordered a comforting hot chocolate. The waiter was sweet; he could obviously see how depressed I was. Well, actually, a mixture of angry and depressed. How has this happened so quickly? How have I gone from young to middle-aged in what seems like just a few years? I suddenly felt over the hill for the first time ever. What a horrible realisation: you are out of the game, you're the older generation now and you've had your fun. Now go and get on with doing something sensible. It's time to grow up and stop lusting after young men in wetsuits. Or is it? I mean, there's no harm in looking, is there? Especially if you're wearing sunglasses.

And as my great-grandmother always used to say, 'A little of what you can't have does you good.' This was a woman who, aged ninety-seven, was lying ill in bed as a young handsome doctor listened to her heart. 'Come any closer and I'll kiss you,' she told him. An inspiration to us all. She also rubbed out the original date on her passport and made herself ten years younger. A trick I will be adopting any day now.

I paid the bill and got up to leave.

'One for the road?' said the caravan-sized (and, in fact, -shaped) waiter. I decided to go shopping instead: the middle-aged woman's consolation prize.

CHAPTER EIGHTEEN

Better Than Death

There's nothing like a trip to Monaco to remind you that there is a grim alternative to ageing: dying. On 13 September 1982, Grace Kelly, award-winning actress and much-admired princess, crashed her Rover P6 on the windy road that leads from France to Monaco. The official version is that she had a stroke, but rumours persist that it was her daughter Stephanie who was driving.

The car rolled one hundred feet down the cliff. Stephanie managed to get out at some stage during the fall, but Grace did not. She ended up in hospital with multiple bone breaks and died of a brain haemorrhage the day after.

Whatever else we do to stay alive there is nothing that can protect us from a horrendous car accident. Although according to a Cambridge professor I met humans can be repaired like cars, or any other machine, by systematically targeting the parts that decay. Dr Aubrey de Grey's theory is that the first person who is going to live to be one thousand years old has already been born. He plans to let people reach peak maturity (around thirty) and then keep them that way, forever.

Every day around 150,000 people die. Two-thirds of those die from ageing. Dr de Grey's argument is that we should look upon ageing as a mass-killer disease that we need to do something about. Dr de Grey says he hopes to get his system up and running within thirty years' time.

'I'll be seventy in thirty years' time so it's too late for me,' I say.

'So will I,' he replies. 'But it's not too late. I will be able to reverse ageing. It's a straightforward repair and maintenance problem, you can take a car that is old to a garage and it can come out looking really good.'

Dr de Grey maintains that exterior signs of ageing such as sagging skin will be a thing of the past. Similarly the brain will stay young as a result of the treatments the body receives.

'A seventy-five-year-old will look, act and most importantly *feel* like a thirty-five-year-old,' he said. After discussing his theories for sometime I was really impressed with the whole concept. I felt like I'd been in the presence of a true visionary.

'Thank you so much for your time,' I said as I left him, 'it's been an honour. I'll be your first guinea pig.'

'No,' he smiled, getting on his bike, 'you don't want to be the first.'

Grace Kelly is buried in Monaco Cathedral. It is not a pretty building; it is rather too large for the place, the size of a small railway station, and seems to have been built with the nineteenth-century equivalent of breeze blocks. The white façade is peppered with arches and columns that sit rather incongruously with the background; they seem too fussy for it. Its position, though, is magnificent: overlooking the Jardins Saint-Martin and the sea.

The elaborately carved wooden confessionals give you a choice of relating your sins in either French or Italian. It reminds me of those tourist shops that announce that 'English is spoken here'.

I walk around the cathedral, looking for Princess Grace's final resting place. There are various altars dedi-cated to saints. One is in memory of Padre Pio, whom my Italian grandmother was mad about. She even had a poster of him on her kitchen wall, rather like a teenage girl has a poster of a pop star.

It is not easy to spot Grace's grave among the many identical tombstones of other Grimaldi family members, which are laid out in a semicircular pattern around the altar, starting with the early princes of Monaco. They all look the same; plain marble with red engraved writing, stating the name of the person and the dates and an engraved royal crest. They melt into the floor, creating a totally flat surface. Princess Grace's is the one with all the flowers on it, second from last. After Grace's is Prince Rainier's, and then they run out of space. Maybe Prince Albert thinks he will live for ever. Perhaps that is why he is encouraging conferences on anti-ageing, like the one I'm here to attend.

Grace Kelly had a fairy-tale early life. She was a Hollywood film star who married a prince. Her eleven films include the classics, *High Noon*, *Dial M for Murder*, *Rear Window*, *To Catch a Thief*, and *High Society*, which she made in 1956, the year she married Prince Rainier.

I walk out of the cathedral and up towards the royal palace. As I make my way along a tiny winding road, with almost non-existent pavements, called the rue Colonel Bellando de Castro, I think about the fact that for some, dying young has been a good career move. Princess Diana, Marilyn Monroe, James Dean, along with Grace Kelly, will all be remembered as young and beautiful. It's an odd thing, but as you get older, the heroes of your youth get younger. Soon James Dean will start to look the same age as my stepson – how scary is that? A friend of mine's father died when he was in his thirties. When she looks at the last picture taken of him she is struck by the fact that she is now older than he was at the time.

Suddenly a policeman on a motorbike swerves around the corner, lights flashing, motioning me to move out the way.

I narrowly miss being run over by a vast black Mercedes carrying Prince Albert himself. I know it's him for two reasons: one, I read *Paris Match*, so recognise him and know all about his love child, and two, his photograph is in all the windows of all the shops in Monaco.

I am beyond excited at seeing Prince Albert and immediately text my husband.

'It is hardly surprising you saw him, he does live there,' is his response. 'Now go and do some work.'

He is not in a good mood with me. My arrival home was not quite as positive as I had hoped it would be. Rupert and the children met me at the airport. The girls loved my hair and rather amazingly didn't seem to notice the lips.

'Is it safe to kiss you or are they catching?' was Rupert's first question.

'So you don't like them?' I asked, disappointed.

'No. You look like one of those silly women we're always laughing about.'

We walked to the car in silence. 'Are they permanent?' he asked, in what I thought was a rather calm manner. Surely, if he really thought they were permanent, he would be semi-hysterical?

'Oh, no, three to six months,' I said cheerfully, piling the children into the car. 'And in a couple of days the swelling will go down more and I will look almost back to normal.'

'I wonder if you'll ever be normal,' said Rupert.

That evening we had a lovely family dinner together. I cooked pasta, we drank our favourite wine and the children were thrilled with all their presents from America. Bea looked especially fabulous in her black and white cow-print coat from Kitson Kids, where Lisa and I went after our lunch at the Ivy. Apparently Angelina Jolie and Jennifer Aniston shop there. Though probably not at the same time.

It was great to be home. Rupert talked about his new book deal. He had just signed a contract to write a book about water. I thought that was brilliant and started coming up with some ideas for it. He just stared at me.

'What is it?' I asked. 'Don't you like any of this?'

'I like your thoughts,' he said. 'But I just can't take you seriously with those lips.'

Mary's reaction the following day at the school gates was no more enthusiastic. 'Is that supposed to be sexy?' she asked, staring at my lips in disbelief.

But after a week at home the lips were actually looking fairly sane, and I got more used to them, even if no one else was. I actually started growing quite fond of them. They were a nice shape, although there remain two slight bumps that shouldn't be there. Rupert still wasn't convinced, though. He liked the teeth, couldn't see any difference to the stomach, but hated the lips. He was keener on the hair, mainly because, as he said, 'It makes you happy.'

Monaco is about the same size as Hyde Park. After the Vatican it is the world's smallest independent state. It has more millionaires per capita than any other country in the world, so I guess if you were looking for someone to pay for all your anti-ageing treatments, this would be as good a place to start as any.

This weekend the tiny principality is busier than usual. It is the fifth Anti-Ageing Medicine World Congress. Delegates from many countries are gathered at this trade fair to hear the latest methods of staying young for as long as is humanly possible. Providing you don't get run over by Prince Albert. Anti-ageing medicine is big business. As Natasha Singer points out in an article in the *New York Times*, after the war on drugs, crime, terror and AIDS, we now have the war on ageing. (And we all know which is scarier.) Ageing, which was once seen as a fact of life, is now being fought with the same vigour as cancer.

It is almost exactly a year since I began my investigation into what you can do to stay young (-looking), and so it seems fitting that my first session brings me back to where I began: breasts.

Throughout my year of research, I have asked just about every plastic surgeon and dermatologist how you can avoid the décolletage ageing. They all say that it is one of the most difficult areas, due to the fact that the skin is fine, thin and very delicate. Living in the south of France I see so many women of a certain age who may have looked after their faces but whose décolletage gives the game away. It's one of the best places, along with the hands, to determine how old someone really is. The wrinkles just sit on the décolletage, a reminder of every moment they forgot to put on sunscreen or lay on a beach. And it's not only wrinkles that are a problem: there are the brown sun spots and the skin tone too.

Luckily Monsieur Stéphane Auroy from Saint-Germain in Paris is at the conference to tell us about rejuvenation techniques for the décolletage. He talks a lot of sense and my décolletage is already feeling better by the time he's finished.

If you're worried about your décolletage here are your options. First and foremost, wearing sunscreen. Second, moisturising the area, either through creams or treatments like mesotherapy. As you may remember, I had this on my face and loved it. It is basically hyaluronic acid injected into the skin to give it moisture. Another possibility is Botoxing some of the lines, maybe combining a Botox treatment with a mesotherapy treatment. Then you could move on to lasers, so-called IPL (intense pulsed light) treatments, perhaps combined with a peeling treatment. Finally, and most effectively, according to Monsieur Auroy, there are bi-polar radio-frequency treatments which conduct heat to the epidermis. The latter are all well and good if you have the time, money and access to a good dermatologist, the first two are much more easily achievable. I, for one, will be smearing my décolletage area with creams on an hourly basis from now on, and cleansing regularly with the same products I use for my face. Or maybe the charming Monsieur Auroy might like to do it?

At every conference there is a star, one person everyone has come to see, a pioneer in his or her field, an icon. At this conference that star is Sydney Coleman, a New York-based plastic surgeon who pioneered fat grafting techniques to use them as fillers, which he has patented under the name LipoStructure and performed over 3,000 times during the past seventeen years.

Sydney is very much the star I expected. He is confident, his presentation slick and his manner humorous and engaging. His message is fascinating. You can take fat from your hips, thighs, stomach, wherever, and inject it into your tits. How often has this fantasy crossed my mind? How many times have I wished I could just pick up my stomach and slap it on my tits? Obviously not now I've been SmartLipoed by Dr LookGood, but you get the message. I don't believe there is a woman out there with less than a D cup that would be averse to a little fat redistribution. Sydney, I'm all ears.

'Due to the great success I had in body contouring using lipofilling I decided to look at using the same method for breasts,' he begins. 'We are taught as plastic surgeons to replace like with like wherever possible. In other words, use the patient's own tissue.' He shows us a photo of a woman (a very thin woman) and tells us that he was able to harvest 'an unbelievably good yield' of fat from her and inject it into her breast. It sounds like he's talking about a wheat field. But the results are great; her breast looks natural and full, and of course there's nothing fake in there, just some of her own fat, so I guess they probably feel pretty real too.

Sydney goes on to tell us how useful fat grafting is to disguise existing implants that can sometimes have very obvious edges. He shows us a pair of what he called 'Las Vegas-type breasts' before and after. They still looked awful, but at least there were no edges.

So far, all this is sounding promising. Way back in Switzerland at the beginning of my search, I asked Dr Derder if there was any way to increase the size of the breast or lift them without cutting them open. There wasn't, he told me. So I resigned myself to a life-time of too small breasts. The American writer Nora Ephron once said that she honestly believes that if she'd had bigger breasts she would have been a different person. I agree with her. Big breasts make you feel sexy, feminine, attractive and, well, just shaggable really. A bit like hair extensions; I mean you can't possibly be a bad lay with all that HAIR! So I have always secretly (actually, not even that secretly) yearned for bigger boobs. Is fat grafting the answer to my prayers? What's the downside?

For one, you can only really go up by one cup size. Well, that's not the end of the world. Second, you need to go through an enormous amount of liposuction to harvest the fat and that means going under general anaesthetic, as well as lots of pain and bruising where the fat originated from afterwards. Third, the breast-enlargement then takes between four and seven hours as the fat has to be injected incredibly slowly.

'There are people who will do it quicker,' says Sydney. 'But they won't get the same results. If you just squirt fat into the breast you will end up with problems like fat cysts.'

This is another downside. Fat injected into the breast can calcify or form a cyst. At worst it can mimic a breast cancer lump.

The American Society for Aesthetic Plastic Surgery doesn't recommend fat grafting as a solution to your small-breast problem 'in the interests of safety'. Listening to all the downsides, my excitement has waned considerably. It's all a bit too macabre. It certainly isn't for me.

Next we have a description of breast reduction using liposuction techniques. This is given by Loek Habbema from the Netherlands, who shows us a video of the procedure, which starts with the patient putting her ample breast into a jug of water.

'This may seem primitive,' says the doctor. 'But it's a very effective way of measuring volume.' Then we watch as he pumps the breast full of liquid (the same painkilling liquid I had pumped into me for my SmartLipo). The poor woman (who is awake during the whole thing) watches her breasts turn into two melons, almost as big as her head. He uses a powered cannula to extract the fat. If I were ever to consider a breast reduction, then this seems a fairly pain-free method, which has the added advantage of harvesting fat you can then use in some other part of your body should you ever need it. Also, after the procedure the breasts 'lift' by an average of 2.8 per cent.

There is a real buzz around the next presentation. A distinguished-looking Swede arrives. There is a delay while he insists on installing his Apple Mac (everyone else has been using the Sony VAIO provided). Once the technical side is running smoothly, he tells us that he has just completed the first ever experiment using hyaluronic acid to restore volume in the breast. This is what I have been thinking about since I started all this. Why, if it is possible to use fillers (which is just another word for hyaluronic acids) on the face, lips, etc., is it not possible to inject them into the breast and, hey breasto, end up with bigger tits in a jiffy and no invasive surgery?

According to Dr Hedén it soon will be. His experiment involved nineteen female patients with an average age of thirty-one, who were injected with a maximum of 100 ml of Macrolane (a kind of hyaluronic acid) into the breast. The results were a 95 per cent patient satisfaction rate. He shows us before and after pictures, which are impressive. The breasts look rounded, natural and totally untouched. He tells us one of the patients from the pilot study liked having bigger breasts so much she has now gone on to have implants.

The fact that it is not permanent is both an upside and a downside to hyaluronic acid. The body eventually absorbs it. So you will have bigger boobs for a total of about two years but they gradually go back to their original size. The upside is that you aren't stuck with them. If you get your lips done and you look like the Bride of Wildenstein you know that in a few months' time you'll be back to normal, unlike injecting silicone, which is with you for life.

'If anything should go wrong,' adds the Swede, 'Macrolane is easy to remove.'

But before you all rush off to get this done, it's not available yet and probably won't be for a number of years. And when it is available, I'm first in the queue.

'We need further clinical studies, so it is difficult to

say when it will be available for consumer use,' Dr Hedén tells me when I catch up with him on the escalator after his talk. (Did you think I was going to let this man get away?) 'But we are making good progress and I am looking in the next trials at administering the injection under local and not general anaesthetic.'

Now you're talking. The disadvantage is that you can't get a really dramatic size increase (yet). But personally I'd already be happy with a cup size.

A talk entitled 'Suspension Threads for Breasts' is given by Marlen and George Sulamanidze, a father and son team from T'bilisi in Georgia. They show us their mastopexy methods, which involve threading the breast and attaching the threads, creating a hypodermic bra holding the breast up. Compared with the methods we have seen earlier, the sight of a fifteen-centimetre needle being pushed in and out of the breast with thick black thread looping around it looks positively medieval. One series of pictures they show has the treated breast sticking straight up like an upside-down ice-cream cone and the other one looking actually quite normal. The videos are almost unwatchable, the whole process seems barbaric. I am in an audience of doctors, but I can sense that even they don't want to look.

The chairman keeps interrupting them, telling them

not to speak at once. The father, who speaks not a word of English, is busy bossing his son about, who is doing his very best (and he only looks about eighteen) to deal with the presentation, the grumpy chairman and the autocratic father. He is all dressed up in his best suit and I feel sorry for them both, really. Eventually the chairman just tells them to get off the stage, interrupting the son in mid-flow, saying that their time is up. What a waste of their time to come all the way from T'bilisi to be shouted at. But it made everyone else look so much better, including the final speaker, who is there to present the BRAVA method of breast rejuvenation.

He is a Frenchman wearing a black suit and an open-necked white shirt. He slightly reminds me of a member of The Jam, but he's more clean-shaven and better-looking. The BRAVA method is what is known as a vacuum-assisted breast augmentation method. Simply put, it causes tension in the existing tissue, thus making it grow. This is the method for those of you who believe in enhancing your bodies but only through natural methods. You wear plastic bowls over your breasts for a minimum of ten hours a day (yep, that's the downside) for between ten and twenty-six weeks and at the end of that period you will (theoretically) find that your breasts have got bigger.

The problem is that although the handsome

Frenchman had very good pictures to demonstrate the effects of his method, the results from his study are not scientifically conclusive and I'm not sure I want to put myself (and my breasts) through ten hours of vacuuming a day for six months to find there is no difference.

I'm done with breasts and décolletages, and it's time for a break anyway. I walk into the exhibition hall of the Forum Grimaldi, where hundreds of anti-ageing companies are displaying their wares. Most obvious are all the companies selling various types of fillers. These include Restylane from Sweden, the first to market hyaluronic acid. Now there are a whole host of others that do more or less the same thing including Teosal, Isogel, Voluma, Evolence, Surgiderm, Juvederm, Outline, Natural Face Balance and many more. One scary fact, and something to keep in mind, is that in Europe no clinical studies are required before any of these products can hit the consumer market.

There are also a number of machines on display that look like R2D2 from Star Wars. They are called things like Fraxel, Calipso, Matripor and Thermalipo. They promise to do various things such as tighten skin, remove cellulite and recontour the body safely and efficiently. The new buzz-phrase seems to be 'no down-time', so you can come in during your lunch break and leave with a new backside before your boss has even noticed you've left your desk.

There is a stall advertising a treatment called Aqua-rejuvenation, which interests me because it seems at least vaguely natural. According to the manufacturers you can achieve skin rejuvenation by high water pressure. It looks like a microdermabrasion machine and the representative tells me that in fact it starts with microdermabrasion before a solution made up of water and one of three mixes (anti-ageing, bleaching or anti-acne) is sprayed on the skin using a water-beam.

It sounds just like the Simonin treatment I had in Switzerland almost a year ago. It suddenly occurs to me that all these anti-ageing treatments are more or less the same, however unique or new they pretend to be. They are either heating your dermis to activate your fibro-blasts and collagen, or taking a layer of skin off, or plumping it up with fillers or fat, or stretching it with surgery. They all claim to have great results and to be unique, but they all boil down to the principles I mention. Everyone is selling the same old stuff really.

'Hello, how lovely to see you.' A blond man shakes my hand vigorously. It's Dr Miracle from the HB Clinic in London. 'I have so much to tell you. Come with me.' He drags me off towards a corner of the room.

'There is new research to suggest that dairy products actually cause osteoporosis,' he tells me breathlessly.
'And we shouldn't eat cereals either, but all this will be
suppressed by the multinationals. Just think about it:
our ancestors didn't eat any of that.'

'What are we supposed to eat then?'

'I know, it's impossible, isn't it? Also they are discov-
ering that cholesterol is actually necessary, that hormones
come from it, and lack of hormones is one of the major
factors that causes wrinkles. Our hormones start depleting
aged around twenty to twenty-five. You see how men get
bellies? Well, that doesn't just come from the sky! It's a
reduction of growth hormone and testosterone. But
heaven forbid you get fat. Stop! Don't move,' he
commands, holding my face.

'Oh my God, what is it?' Have I suddenly come up
in a conference-induced rash?

'One day I will do this for you,' he says, pointing
at my jaw-line. 'And these.' He strokes the lines next to
my nose, which are technically known as your nasolabial
folds. 'How old are you?'

'Thirty-eight,' I tell him, crossing my fingers behind
my back.

'That's the age you need to really start thinking about
things. Although you look quite good,' he adds hastily.

'Thanks,' I say, but actually I'm not sure I want to see him again, much as I like him. A kind of rebellion is starting to well up inside me. Suddenly I feel a bit sick. The conference is almost too overwhelming, filled with obsessive people hysterically chasing – or capitalising on – our eternal search for youth and wrinkle-free skin. I just don't think I can take any more anti-ageing at the moment. I have a sudden longing to think about something else, anything else.

Dr Miracle is undeterred. 'You mustn't get fat, you know. With every extra kilo you lose longevity. If you are between ten and fifteen kilos overweight you will not only lose five years of life, but five years of good quality life.'

'What do you think of Thermage?' I ask him.

'I don't like it, I don't like anything that burns the skin. It might look OK now, but who knows what the effect will be in five or ten years? But this,' he points at my jaw again, 'this I can do for you with a new method, it's very exciting.' And then he's gone, skipping off into the mêlée of other delegates looking for the latest foolproof thing to keep their client base forever young.

The lectures are about to start again and I go to one on ageing hair. We are shown a film of a hair transplant. Now here's an interesting fact: did you know that on your body there is only one hair per hair follicle but on your head there are between one and four, and sometimes even more? And have you any idea how repulsive a hair transplant is? No, nor did I, but believe me, it's not a pretty sight. From the extraction of the follicular units to the so-called 'stick and place' procedure of putting them into the scalp. I can't bear to watch any more. If Elton John has gone through this then he's a bigger fool than I thought.

I have to leave the room. I stumble into another lecture theatre where some poor woman is having her buccal fat pads removed, also known as cheek reduction surgery. This is even worse than the hair. Her face is opened up and the fat around her jaw is taken out to give her a more youthful, slim-line look. It's like a horror movie; her face is half face and half cadaver.

'Of course you have to prepare patients for the results,' a doctor is saying. 'Their whole face is going to change, they will no longer look like the same person, but I have found that after three months or so they get used to it and are very happy.'

This to me seems totally obscene. People have their heads opened up so they look like something from the film *The Texas Chainsaw Massacre*. Once they're put together they no longer recognise themselves. But it's all worth the effort as there is some fat missing from their face, which they have probably stored to have inserted into their breasts or buttocks. The eager faces of the audience somehow remind me of a clinic I heard of in LA where they use human foetuses in face packs. Apparently the foetuses come from Russia and women pay hundreds of dollars to plaster them on their skin, which to me epitomises how sick the anti-ageing industry can be.

I take one last look at the screen. I have to get outside before I throw up. I run up the wide stairs of the auditorium. A security guard opens the heavy wooden door to let me out. I walk to the terrace and lean on the railings breathing in the sea air.

It's such a relief to be away from it all. I feel the wind on my cheeks and relish the freshness of it compared to the stultifying and claustrophobic feeling of the conference. It is a beautifully sunny day. It is not hot, but the sun is warming. The air is fresh and invigorating. I take deep breaths, looking out over the sea where the late afternoon sun has the effect of a thousand flashbulbs going off on the surface of the water. There is nothing in that conference hall, no 'miracles' that can ever compare to nature.

For some reason Elizabeth Bennet from *Pride and Prejudice* pops into my head. OK, I know she actually is young, but when she shows up at Netherfield Hall after stomping across the fields to see her sister Jane, Darcy doesn't fall in love with her because she's perfectly made up and groomed with silicone-enhanced lips. He falls in love with her because her cheeks are flushed with country air, she looks pretty, healthy and, above all, natural.

I decide right here, right now, that I've had enough anti-ageing. I walk back to the hotel along the seafront, feeling more invigorated with each step taking me away from the conference. I grab my bags and jump on the next train bound for Montpellier. As I watch the coast whiz by, I catch sight of my reflection in the window. I can't deny that, for the most part, I've been enjoying myself immensely. But what have I been doing all this for? I have constantly used the book as an excuse, but I also wanted to see how far I could go. I wanted to see how much I could change. I wanted to see if I could look younger than I am, if I could look better than I should for my age. I've had a great run but I think it's time to stop. Otherwise, I will be forever trying to catch up with myself. The first thing I should do is to stop lying about my age. It's ridiculous; it's even got to the stage where I almost believe my own lies. At one stage I wondered whether I could just call myself thirty-eight and be done with it. Not budge from that and hope that one day some dozy official would let me get away with actually changing it on my passport. But what for? Is it not time to grow up and face the fact that I am . . . I try mentally practising saying my real age. It's too awful, I just can't.

Rupert meets me at the station.

'You look better,' he says, hugging me. 'The lips are calming down.'

We go for a coffee.

'You know you really don't need all this stuff,' he says, stirring his espresso as I sip my green tea. 'What you need to do is find a look that suits you and that suits your age. All this is just ridiculous. It doesn't make you look better; it just makes you look mad.'

Despite having arrived at a similar conclusion myself, a small part of me rebels at this. He's just saying that because he doesn't want his wife wandering around looking like she's ready to kiss anyone who might get in her way, I think. How can natural be the only answer? If that was the case, no one would bother and the whole anti-ageing industry would simply collapse. I know I ran out on the extremes of the conference, but I also feel a lot better and younger-looking for all my efforts over the past twelve months.

'It's not elegant,' Rupert goes on, 'and it's not your style. I don't know who you're doing it for, but it certainly isn't me. I mean, your hair is all very well, but I can't even run my fingers through it because it's full of glue. And the lips, well, they're much better now, and there was maybe one moment when I thought they were quite intriguing, but only in the way that fake breasts are. You don't actually want to live with them.'

I sip my tea and stay silent. He's wrong, part of me thinks. I do look better. I feel better. He's just a kill-joy. I have more hair than all three original Charlie's Angels put together. How can that be a bad thing? Like a recalcitrant child I refuse to agree with what he says, even if he has pinpointed something I am just beginning to realise myself.

CHAPTER NINETEEN

Conclusions

My grandmother always used to say that it is important to go away in order to realise how nice it is to be home. Three months on, I know exactly what she means. This revelation began with a surprising comment from Rupert. We were lying in bed chatting one morning when I caught him staring at me.

'What's wrong?' I asked him, briefly wondering if my lips had started to implode.

'It's your wrinkle,' he said. 'It's come back.' But the tone of his voice was not one of disgust or even disappointment, it sounded like he was greeting a long-lost friend.

I jumped up and looked in the bathroom mirror. Yes, there it was: *the* wrinkle, right in the middle of my forehead, now with its new friend *the* vein. I expected to feel horror, fury, despair, anger. But funnily enough, I was totally calm. I looked at *the* wrinkle a little closer. I frowned and it deepened. So the movement had come back to my forehead.

'I think you look much better with it,' says Rupert. 'Botox doesn't really make you look younger; it just makes you look like a victim of the Age of Botox.'

'The what?'

'The Age of Botox. It comes after the Age of Reason and shortly before the Age of Stupidity. It's when women can no longer express surprise or anger; they are just flat canvases with no ability to show emotions.'

I look at him, taken aback at this philosophical outburst so early in the morning.

'I can tell you're surprised,' he said. 'That's a good thing.'

'You just want me to look old so you can run off with a younger woman,' I say.

'Not this weekend, at least,' says Rupert.

The second thing that happened was that my hair fell out. Not my real hair, but my infusions. I would be wandering around a supermarket and suddenly find an infusion caught by some artichokes I had been eyeing up. The worst time was at a meeting at school to discuss my daughter's performance that term. I got up and found one of my infusions was left on the chair. Hastily I grabbed it, smiled at the bemused teacher and left the room.

This is not Rodolfo's fault (bless him). The infusions should in theory have been removed two to three months after he put them in. Four months later they were still looking good but starting to give up their fight for life. So in the end I covered my head in baby oil and took them all out. It was a terrible task. I had bits of glue everywhere. Added to the depression I felt at removing them was the pain I felt pulling them out. But it was cheaper and quicker than flying to New York.

The first person to see the new hairless me was my friend Anna, the yoga teacher. Anna has only ever seen me with infusions so had no idea what I looked like before.

'My God!' she exclaimed. 'You look ten years younger without all that hair.'

'You're joking,' was my reaction. But actually, I didn't dislike my real hair. It looked in good condition, and even a little livelier than it had before. And of course it had grown a few inches.

Mary, who rather annoyingly has perfect blonde ringlets, looked at me long and hard. I was convinced she would say I was practically bald (which, compared with her, I am).

'I *like* your hair,' she said slowly. 'I really do.'

The strangest thing was the reaction of the children. The girls had been mad about my long, curly hair; I suppose it looked a bit like a Barbie doll's hair. But they begged me not to get extensions again.

'Why?' I asked Olivia.

'We like you better like this,' she said. 'You're prettier, you look more like me.'

Rupert was delighted, of course. 'You look so much better,' he said. 'But I bet you anything you go and get them done again.'

He was right as usual. I simply could not go back to life as a thin-haired person. In fact, even before all the infusions had been painstakingly removed, I had already made an appointment at Richard Ward in London to have more extensions put in.

And despite everyone's reaction, I was determined to go ahead with new extensions. I just didn't believe that I looked better. I didn't mind my hair as much as I thought I would, I didn't hate it like I had before, but I was convinced I would look better with some more of it. So I asked for straight extensions (less Wag-like) and said I didn't want them as long as the ones Rodolfo had put in.

I showed up at the Richard Ward salon for my

appointment at 10 a.m. on a Wednesday morning. By now I was wavering; a nagging voice in my head was telling me that my real hair wasn't too bad and it was certainly a hell of a lot easier to manage. Still I put on the gown and sat in the chair, ready to be transformed. I can always take them out again, I reasoned.

Nicky, the stylist, proudly presented the hair she was about to stick to my head. It was long, thick, glossy and straight. I was going to look great. Suddenly it all seemed like a brilliant idea again. I went off to have my hair washed and then came back to start the four-hour session.

Nicky began to comb my hair. Then she stopped.

'What is it?' I asked her.

'I don't know,' she said, but I caught her faint look of disgust.

'It could be bits of glue,' I offered. 'I took the last lot out myself.'

Nicky carried on combing for a few seconds. 'No,' she said finally. 'It's not glue. You've got head lice. I'm afraid I'm going to have to ask you to leave immediately.'

An experience to add to 'most humiliating moments in my life', such as when I walked all the way through a number 38 bus with one of my breasts exposed (it was in the days when those sleeveless T-shirts with ridiculously large holes for your arms were in fashion).

I slunk out of the salon, cursing my children and feeling like a leper. Did they give me head lice on purpose? Had Rupert planted them in my hair to scupper my plan for long fake hair?

I went to meet Carla, who had left work to come and cheer me up.

'Don't worry,' she said when we met at Sloane Square tube. 'At least now you won't have to have a matching merkin done too.'

'What's a merkin?' I asked.

'Oh dear, that old brain. I'm afraid it's been too starved of seafood and wine,' said Carla. 'A merkin is a false beard, down there,' she added, nodding towards my pelvic area.

I later discovered that merkins were first worn by prostitutes who had shaved off their pubic hair due to lice. So possibly more relevant to me than I had first imagined. I am, of course, referring to the lice.

Carla and I spent the four hours I should have spent in the hair salon shopping. When it was time to get on my Eurostar home I felt rather happy. I was actually relieved to be going home with my own head of hair, even if it was infested with lice. The infusions were lovely but they were actually quite hard work. Washing and drying my hair took an age and once it was dry, I had to spend ages curling it to get it back to its original luscious look. At one stage I actually got so bored curling it I started doing leg-squats at the same time. I challenged myself to carry on until I'd finished with the tongs. I could hardly walk for three days afterwards, which just goes to show how much time I was spending curling someone else's hair. Sleeping was also difficult with all that hair, although I found I rarely needed a pillow. But I would often wake up with a suffocation sensation or feeling like my hair was being pulled out as one of the infusions got caught under either my or Rupert's shoulder.

After a year of researching anti-ageing I now know that it would be possible to change almost every part of my body. I could have any veins in my legs removed, I could have my breasts lifted and enlarged, I could have any brown spots lasered away, I could have all my fat SmartLipoed, I could have a wrinkle-free forehead, a newly shaped jaw, no nasolabial folds at all if I choose, plumper lips, I could have the folds on my eyelids injected with my own fat so they no longer crinkle and I could take supplements to keep my nails in good shape. I could even have labial reconstruction. I kid you not, there are clinics all over the world offering women an operation which makes your genitalia look like they've never been touched nor had a baby's head force its way through them.

But you know what? I'm not going to. I have learned a lot from my research over the past year, but the most important thing I have learned is that for me going to hell in high heels means victory over old age by staying elegant, sane-looking and true to myself. As well as being healthy and mentally sharp. I am certainly *never* going to give up trying to look as good as I possibly can. But I am going to give up trying to look twenty, or even thirty. I don't ever want to become one of those 1661 women.

I have also learned that while trying to look good for your age is one thing, a desperate obsession with ageing is unhealthy. We grow old and the best we can hope for is to do it in style, obviously using whatever helps you along the way, but with some degree of acceptance. As my friend Frida in Los Angeles says, 'Stop comparing yourself with women half your age. It's just not healthy.'

Germaine Greer says in an article in the *Guardian* that 'whatever you do, you won't look younger. Your body strong or weak has clearly been lived in. The old structure might be in immaculate condition, meticulously maintained, no dry or wet rot, well water-tight, foundations propped up, but then, there's always the wiring.

You could explode, in a shower of synaptic sparks.' This is a little pessimistic, and I think some people would use it as an excuse just to give up, but there is a certain truth in the underlying thought. Whatever you do, you're rotting somewhere, it is simply the course of nature. Like me. I got rid of *the* wrinkle (temporarily) but ended up with a socking great vein in the middle of my forehead instead. And it shows no signs of going away. My lips were enhanced, but even now, months later, I have a small lump on my bottom lip, a stark reminder that there are always consequences to your actions. And where does it all end? Once you start it's rather like doing up one room in the house and then hating all the others. So once you do the Botox, what about your neck? Then your boobs look a bit droopy compared with your neck and face and so on all the way down to your toes until it's time to start all over again. Also you're still going to get old, even if you think you look sixteen. And people will realise that, just like the boy on Venice Beach, who looked at me and then looked away when he realised that I wasn't actually his generation, or even his mother's. As the plastic surgeon Mr Ghengis tells Ruth in Fay Weldon's *The Life and Loves of a She Devil*, 'I can stop you looking old, but you will *be* old.'

One of the most sensible people I met at the conference in Monaco was an Indian businessman who was there because every male member of his family has died before the age of fifty-seven, either from a heart attack or cancer. 'That means I only have twelve years to go,' he told me as we wandered around Monaco Casino, debating whether or not to go in and try our luck at the tables. 'And I'm not ready to die that soon.' Makes you think, eh?

There are many pieces of advice and good practices I've taken away with me from my quest. I will exercise every day if I can, as that seems to me the key to ageing well. I still do the sun salutes Alain taught me every morning, six on each side. And I do some Pilates moves whenever the mood takes me. I have found that just the breathing seems to help keep my tummy firm, so if I'm stuck in a traffic jam, I focus on breathing in and pushing all the air out. Sometimes I can hear Nico's voice in my head, saying, 'Veeeerrrry gooooood.'

Exercise and diet are absolutely crucial. If you do nothing else but exercise and eat well, I would say it's about the best start you can give yourself. About 70 per cent of how you age is genetic and the rest is up to you: how well you eat and how much you exercise, how much care (and to some extent money) you spend on looking after your skin through cleansing, moisturising, using sunscreen religiously and so on. Of course, however genetically perfect you are, if you smoke and eat nothing but Nutella you're going to age badly. Looking good requires an effort, for sure. You just have to decide whether and where you want to make that effort.

I will try to avoid sugar, eat more fruit and vegetables and try my best not to drink too much wine (with the exception, of course, of wine containing resveratrol). I will try to keep out of the sun as much as possible. Tina tells me that to age gracefully, 'forget putting your face in the sun, ever. There's no debate.' For me, this is a little like my father-in-law with the alcohol. Putting my face in the sun is one of my favourite things. So I guess I will have to make a choice, now that I know the effects, as to what is more important: enjoying the feeling of the sun and the wellbeing it gives me, or avoiding wrinkles.

I will try to reduce my stress levels and try to laugh more. Since my laughter yoga experience I have tried the fake laughing, when I'm alone in the car and stuck in a traffic jam or other stress-inducing situation. It's tough – I always imagine there is a secret camera filming me and that if I carry on trying to laugh at nothing the men in white coats will show up and drag me away. But then at least I will be kept out of the sun.

I will do things that I know help prevent ageing,

like moisturise my skin, cleanse it and exfoliate it. I will have a facial either at home or, if I can afford it, at a beautician's. I will use a retinol cream every night and a serum mixed with an antioxidant like a vitamin C powder every morning. And of course I won't leave the bathroom without sunscreen on.

I will try to find the time to be well groomed, to do my nails, my eyebrows, floss my teeth and curl my eyelashes. I will stick to my vow of never going under general anaesthetic for vanity, but if the dashing Swede comes up with a painless way to have bigger breasts I might try it, just for fun. But it won't really make any difference to my life if he doesn't.

I will make an effort to keep those neural pathways moving and open to new experiences; try not to grimace every time I hear loud music or see someone wearing a skirt that starts and ends at the hips. I suppose with three children and two stepchildren that won't be difficult: there will be plenty of exposure to dreadful music and strange fashions. Actually, just living with Rupert keeps my neural pathways moving. He has an extremely varied musical collection, which seems to be getting more eccentric every year. Our house is going through a punk revival at the moment, and I can't say I'm enjoying it. My Take That CDs seem to have mysteriously vanished, along with

Mika, Robbie Williams and James Blunt. But in the interests of my neural pathways, I will not complain.

I will do what Rupert's grandmother did and never give in if I can't remember something: If you let your brain get lazy you're doomed, she would say. She lived until she was ninety-seven and would probably still be alive today, reading her beloved *Daily Mail* (which she called 'her' paper) and giving me good advice, if she hadn't broken her knee and ended up in an English hospital where the MSRS bug killed her.

I will try not to sleep on my side, although I know this is next to impossible. But instead of fretting every time I see a wrinkle appear or a sun spot grow larger I will try to adopt the Laguna Beach approach to stress and howl with laughter. I will remember that while looking ten years younger than you are is doable and admirable, trying to look twenty years younger makes you look ridiculous. And I will remember that there are people who would give anything to age, however disgracefully.

I have gone full circle during the year I have been working on this book. I started out thinking I was all for ageing with grace. I spurned the idea of invasive treatments like fillers and Botox. Then I discovered the fun of faking it and was seduced by the promise of the treatments on offer. Looking back on it, it seems somewhat radical and impulsive to pile into fake lips and liposuction. But I really wanted to see if they worked. And I suppose the book gave me the excuse to try them and pretend I wasn't just being vain. My lips are now almost back to normal. Do I miss the bigger ones? No. But did a small and deeply superficial part of me enjoy being a pouting lunatic for a month or so? Yes, absolutely. Would I do my lips again? Probably not. But I will carry with me a lip-boosting gloss at all times.

I am now past the allure of treatments once more, although I will not discount anything new and exciting that comes on the market, such as the breast-enhancing injections. I'm not *that* past the allure.

But I suddenly realised that by putting myself through them I wasn't actually doing myself enough favours. I didn't actually look any better. I was just under an illusion that I looked better, and the scary thing was that, rather like an alcoholic who can't imagine that life is possible without a drink, I had begun to believe I would be a lesser person without my new teeth, hair, lips, forehead and midriff.

In the end, though, ageing is inevitable and, done with grace, it can actually be quite sexy. Now that I am forty . . . two (there, I said it!) there are certain looks that just don't suit me. Big lips, big hair and a boob-tube is probably one of them. My plan was to face my forties head on, to fight the wrinkles and to emerge the winner. I might not have fought the wrinkles successfully, but I have realised that being sexy and attractive is not necessarily all about being young-looking. It is about being happy with who you are, about looking the best you can and about taking care of yourself on a daily basis. Possibly with a little help from a treatment from time to time. I loved the Botox when I had it and, who knows, maybe I will go for it again one day.

But the key is to find your own ageing level, to find what works for you. And to realise the more extreme measures you resort to in the fight against your wrinkles, the more they will come at a cost, financially and possibly physically, as with me and the vein.

A friend of mine, an artist called Simon Fletcher, says that the only good thing about getting older is 'not having to worry about money'. This is no consolation to me as I will always find something to worry about, unless I'm at Goldeneye in Jamaica sipping a large cocktail on my private beach! But I would say there are other compensations. In my case, more confidence, knowing what I like and what I don't like, being able to appreciate things through experience and knowledge like a beautiful painting, piece of music or a good book, getting

to a stage in my career where I can do what really interests me (like trying different face creams), watching my children grow up, watching my parents grow up (even more amusing), an equilibrium, more serenity and less hair on my legs. Yes, I have discovered the one upside to ageing. The hairs on your legs don't grow as much.

Using everything I have learnt over the past year I have set up an anti-ageing spa retreat with Tina Richards and Anna Cooper, a yoga teacher and psychotherapist. For more information visit www.renewretreats.co.uk.

If this book becomes a bestseller I'll book myself into the Clinique La Prairie for a stay every six months. I have never looked as good or felt as good as I did after three days there. If I can I shall retire there, look fifty when I'm sixty, go for long walks along the lake, watch the swans glide around on the smooth surface, wear purple and smile that perfect Swiss white smile.

Even if I can't do that I will make efforts to stay young every day. I will do sun salutes and Pilates in the mornings before a breakfast of blueberries and muesli, go for long walks wearing a hat to protect myself from the sun while listening to house music on my iPod in the afternoon, drink green tea constantly and end the day with a moisturising bath and exfoliating mask. And, most crucially, wear obscenely high heels at every given opportunity.

ACKNOWLEDGEMENTS

A vast thank you to all the people who generously gave me so much of their time, as well as anti-ageing tips and treatments. A huge thank you to Tina Richards for her sound advice and unparalleled expertise, to everyone at HB Health in London and Steven Victor, Erik Berger and Patty Mayer in the US.

Thank you to my agent, Lizzy Kremer, at David Higham Associates, publisher, Nikola Scott, and Emma Rose at Arrow Books for their encouragement, great editing and enthusiasm.

Thank you to my friend Carla McKay for reminding me that letting your hair (or indeed someone else's hair) down now and again is also anti-ageing.

As always the biggest thank you goes to Rupert, my husband and favourite editor, whom I look forward to growing old with.